Pengu... 🐧 Readers

GW00656736

...**...WAY**

## VIRGINIA WOOLF

**LEVEL**

**7**

RETOLD BY KATE WILLIAMS

ILLUSTRATIONS BY GUY HARVEY

SERIES EDITOR: SORREL PITTS

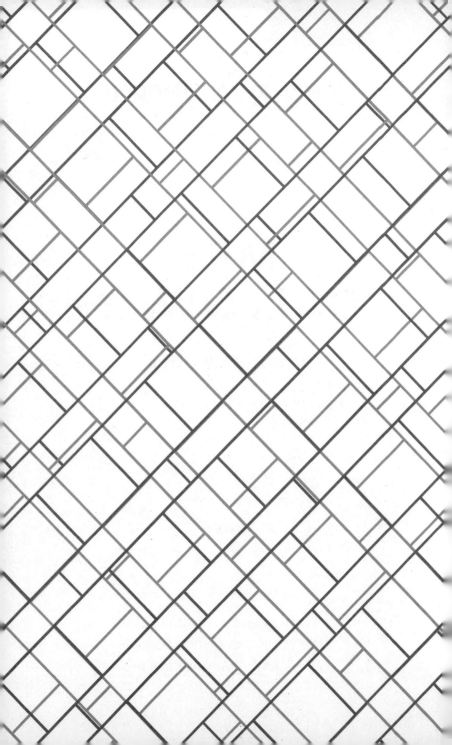

PENGUIN BOOKS

UK | USA | Canada | Ireland | Australia
India | New Zealand | South Africa

Penguin Books is part of the Penguin Random House group of companies
whose addresses can be found at global.penguinrandomhouse.com.
www.penguin.co.uk    www.puffin.co.uk    www.ladybird.co.uk

Penguin Readers edition of *Mrs Dalloway* published by Penguin Books Ltd, 2021
001

Original text written by Virginia Wolf
Text for Penguin Readers edition adapted by Kate Williams
Text for Penguin Readers edition copyright © Penguin Books Ltd, 2021
Illustrated by Guy Harvey
Cover illustration by Leanne Shapton
Illustrations copyright © Penguin Books Ltd, 2021
Cover image copyright © Penguin Books Ltd, 2012

Set in 11/16 pt Baskerville
Typeset by Jouve (UK), Milton Keynes
Printed and bound in Great Britain by Clays Ltd, Elcograf S.p.A.

The authorized representative in the EEA is Penguin Random House Ireland,
Morrison Chambers, 32 Nassau Street, Dublin D02 YH68

A CIP catalogue record for this book is available from the British Library

ISBN: 978–0–241–52080–2

All correspondence to:
Penguin Books
Penguin Random House Children's
One Embassy Gardens, 8 Viaduct Gardens,
London SW11 7BW

MIX
Paper from
responsible sources
FSC® C018179

Penguin Random House is committed to a
sustainable future for our business, our readers
and our planet. This book is made from Forest
Stewardship Council® certified paper.

# Contents

Note about the story      6

Before-reading questions      9

Map of London      10

Mrs Dalloway      11

During-reading questions      102

After-reading questions      108

Exercises      109

Project work      116

Glossary      118

# Note about the story

Virginia Woolf (1882–1941), one of the world's most important writers, was part of the early twentieth century movement of Modernism, which included other types of art such as music and painting. *Mrs Dalloway* (1925) is the fourth of her seven novels.

In Modernist novels, the writer mostly examines the **inner**\* lives of characters, rather than developing a plot in which many things happen. In *Mrs Dalloway* there are no chapters; instead there are sections which follow a particular character and their thoughts. This way of writing is known as a "stream of consciousness" because it shows thoughts running through someone's mind like a river. It includes memories of the past, reactions to the present and plans for the future, as these things come into the character's mind. Sometimes we move between these different times, or between different characters' minds, within a sentence or a paragraph. Reading *Mrs Dalloway* is sometimes like reading a poem; Woolf often uses images to compare things. For example, an image on page 11 compares the air to "the kiss of a wave". Words and phrases are often repeated to build ideas and make connections between characters. The sentences are sometimes long and the way they are written can reflect their meaning. For example, on page 12 the words in brackets [(*but that might be* . . .)] create a pause, and on

---

\* Definitions of words in **bold** can be found in the glossary on pages 118–125.

page 18 there is one phrase after another like a wave rising [*Nonsense, nonsense . . .*]. Often the things that people say aloud are written as reported speech, for example on page 13 when Clarissa and Hugh are talking about Evelyn.

*Mrs Dalloway* is set in London on a single June day in 1923, five years after the end of the First World War (1914–18). We follow three main characters – Clarissa Dalloway, Peter Walsh and Septimus Warren Smith.

Clarissa is the **upper-class** wife of a politician, Richard Dalloway. The Dalloways live in Westminster, in a grand house with servants, including a cook. Clarissa grew up at Bourton, a large country house with gardens, which, unlike the many real places mentioned in London (see Map of London on page 10), Woolf has invented. Clarissa has recently had **influenza** in the deadly 1918–1920 **flu pandemic**, which affected millions of people around the world.

Westminster is the home of the Houses of Parliament, which includes the House of Commons, where elected **Members of Parliament** like Richard Dalloway work, and the famous clock tower known as Big Ben, after its biggest bell. Big Ben **strikes** every quarter of an hour, and also once for each hour on the hour.

Buckingham Palace is the home of the British royal family. In 1923 the king was George V, his wife was Queen Mary and their son, Edward (later Edward VIII) was the Prince of Wales.

Peter Walsh has just returned from five years in India, which in 1923 was part of the British Empire, under British rule. Britain had a large army in India.

Septimus Warren Smith fought in the First World War. Many war memorials were later built to remember the dead, including the Cenotaph, in Whitehall, in 1920.

Septimus is suffering from serious mental illness as a result of his experiences in the war. Like Septimus, Woolf suffered periods of serious mental illness and was treated by doctors with little understanding of her condition. She killed herself in March 1941.

One of Septimus's doctors, Sir William Bradshaw, works in Harley Street, which is famous for its private doctors. He has the title "Sir" because he has been given a special award by the King for his achievements, and his wife is known as Lady Bradshaw.

# Before-reading questions

1 Read the "Note about the story" on page 6, and look at the map on page 10. Look online, and find out more about Westminster. What do you think it was like to live there in 1923? How might it have been different from today?

2 Clarissa Dalloway is the wife of a politician – a Member of Parliament. What do you think life was like for women like her in 1923? Show what you think by imagining a day in Clarissa's life.

3 What do you think happened to soldiers after the end of the First World War? What difficulties do you think they might have had?

4 Read these sentences from the first four paragraphs of *Mrs Dalloway* (pages 11 and 12), and look at the second paragraph of the "Note about the story" again.

(i) Mrs Dalloway said she would buy the flowers herself.

(ii) For Lucy had more than enough to do.

(iii) She was looking at the flowers, at the trees with smoke rising through them, at the birds rising and falling. She was standing and looking until Peter Walsh said, "Daydreaming among the vegetables?" – was that it? Or did he say "I prefer men to cauliflowers?" Was that what he said?

(iv) She was like a bird, blue-green, light, full of life.

Then answer the questions in your notebook:

a In (i) to (iv), whose point of view is it?

b Which sentences are about the present day?

c Where do we move between the past and the present?

d Where is there an image, and what is it an image of ? Do you think that the image is helpful in describing Mrs Dalloway? Why/Why not?

# Map of London

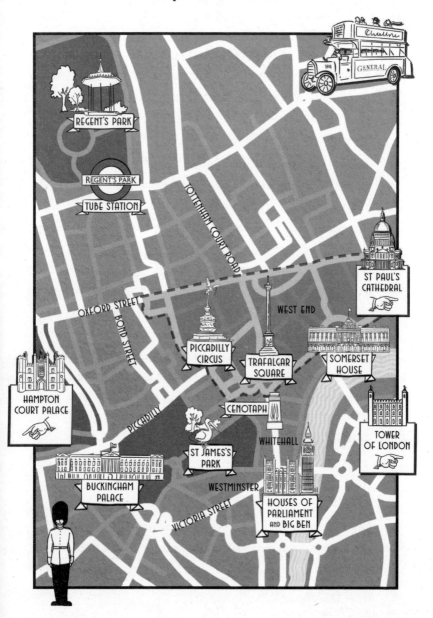

# Mrs Dalloway

Mrs Dalloway said she would buy the flowers herself.

For Lucy had more than enough to do. The doors would be taken off for the party; Rumpelmayer's men were coming to do it. And then, thought Clarissa Dalloway, what a morning – fresh as if presented to children on a beach.

What fun! What a **plunge**! For that's how it had always seemed to her, when she had thrown open the **French windows** at Bourton and **plunged** into the open air. There, it was stiller, quieter than this, of course. How fresh, how calm the air was in the early morning, like the kiss of a wave, cool and sharp. And yet it was **solemn** (for a girl of eighteen as she had then been), standing there and feeling that something awful was about to happen. She was looking at the flowers, at the trees with smoke rising through them, at the birds rising and falling. She was standing and looking until Peter Walsh said, "Daydreaming among the vegetables?" – was that it? Or did he say "I prefer men to cauliflowers?" Was that what he said? He must have said it early one morning when she had gone out into the garden. Peter Walsh. He would be back from India soon – June or July, she forgot which, for his letters were awfully dull. It was his sayings that **one** remembered; and his eyes, his pocket-knife, his smile, his moods. And how strange it was, when millions of things had disappeared, to remember a few sayings like this about cabbages.

She paused at the edge of the pavement, waiting for a van to pass. A **charming** woman, her neighbour Scrope Purvis thought her (knowing her as one knows the people who live next door in Westminster). She was like a bird, blue-green, light, full of life, though she was over fifty and he noticed that her hair had turned very white since her illness. There she stood, waiting to cross, perfectly **upright**, never seeing him.

Having lived in Westminster so long – was it twenty years now, or more? – Clarissa felt the beat of calm, a pause, (but that might be her heart, affected by **influenza**, the doctors had told her), before Big Ben sounded. There! First a warning, musical; then the hour, final. We are such fools, she thought, crossing Victoria Street, for loving life so much: these crowds, this noise, this movement. Carriages, motor cars, vans, bands playing in the parks, and the strange high singing of some aeroplane up above. That was what she loved: life, London, this moment of June.

For it was the middle of June. The War was over, except for someone like Lady Bexborough who had opened a church **fête**, they said, with the **telegram** in her hand. John, her favourite, was killed. But it was over, thank Heaven – it was over. It was June. The King and the Queen were at Buckingham Palace. And everywhere, though it was still so early, there was a stirring of life, wrapped in the soft, grey-blue morning air. And she, too, loving it as she did, was a part of it, for that very night she was going to light a **spark**, to give her party.

But how strange the silence was, on entering St James's Park; the **mist** on the lake, the slow-swimming, happy ducks. And there, coming along on some important business, handsome, manly, almost too perfectly dressed, was her old friend Hugh Whitbread – the admirable Hugh!

"Good morning to you, Clarissa!" announced Hugh, rather **extravagantly**, since they had known each other as children. "Where are you going?"

"I love walking in London," said Mrs Dalloway. "Really, it's better than walking in the country."

Hugh and Evelyn were in London, unfortunately, to see doctors. Clarissa could not count the times she had visited Evelyn Whitbread in hospital. Was Evelyn ill again? She was not at all her usual **self**, Hugh told her, not needing to say more, for Clarissa understood at once in her sisterly way. At the same moment she felt oddly **aware** of her hat. Perhaps it was not right for the early morning, was that it? For Hugh always made her feel like a girl of eighteen, as he moved on, raising his own hat rather extravagantly and promising to come to her party. He might be only a little late after the garden party at Buckingham Palace. But she always felt attached to him, having known him so long, and thought him a good man in his way, though Richard was nearly driven mad by him. As for Peter Walsh, he had never to this day forgiven her for liking Hugh.

She could remember **scene** after scene at Bourton – **quarrelling** with Peter. Hugh was never Peter's equal, of course, but was not such a fool as Peter believed. When Hugh's old mother wanted him he went, without a word, unselfishly. Peter would say that Hugh had no heart, no brain, nothing but the **manners** of an English gentleman, but that was just her dear Peter at his worst. He could be impossible, unbearable, but wonderful to walk with on a morning in June like this.

13

For she and Peter could be parted for hundreds of years; (she never wrote him a letter and his were so dull); but suddenly she would wonder – If he were with me now, what would he say? He would not notice the beautiful day, the trees and the grass, and the little girl in pink – Peter never saw a thing of all that. It was the **state** of the world that interested him, and the failings of her own character. How they quarrelled! He said she would marry a Prime Minister and stand at the top of her stairs, greeting her guests, and be the perfect hostess. (She had cried over that in her bedroom.)

So she would find herself in St James's Park, still arguing with herself that she had been right not to marry him. For in marriage there must be a little independence between people living together every day in the same house, which Richard gave her, and she gave him. (Where was Richard this morning, for example? At some government meeting, but she never asked what.) But with Peter everything had to be shared. And it was unbearable. When it came to that scene in the garden by the **fountain**, she had to break with him or they would both have been destroyed; though she had felt the pain for years, like an arrow in her heart. Then there had been the horror of hearing at a concert that he had married a woman he met on the boat going to India! Never would she forget all that! Cold and heartless, he had called her. She would never understand how he cared, he said. And there was no need for her to waste her **pity**. He did not need it, he was perfectly happy, though he had never done anything they talked of. His whole life had been a **failure**. It made her angry still.

She had reached the park gates. She stood for a moment, looking at the buses in Piccadilly.

She would not say of anyone in the world now that they were this or were that. She felt very young; at the same time incredibly old. She had a lasting feeling, as she watched the taxi cabs, of being far, far out to sea and alone; a feeling that it was very, very dangerous to live even one day. Not that she thought herself clever, or anything but ordinary. She knew nothing: no languages, no history; she hardly ever read a book except in bed. Yet she was completely **fascinated** by all this life passing before her; and she would not say of Peter, or of herself, I am this, I am that.

Her only **gift** was knowing at once what people were like, she thought, walking on. She remembered the house at Bourton, full of people, lit up for parties at night; she remembered her sister Sylvia and Sally Seton – such crowds of people dancing all night. But everyone remembered; what she loved was this, here, now, in front of her; the fat lady in the cab. Did it matter then, she asked herself, walking towards Bond Street, that one day all this must go on without her? Did she mind, or was it **comforting** to believe that death was an end? But still she believed that here, there, in the streets of London, somehow she survived, Peter survived. She was part of the trees at home, of the house there, of the people she had never met, laid out like a mist between the people she knew best. Her life, her self, spread far.

But what past was she dreaming of as she looked into the bookshop window, reading Shakespeare's poem about death in the open book?

*Fear no more the heat of the sun*

Death was an end to all fear and joy. This recent age had been for them all a fountain of tears. They had met suffering with courage, been upright. Think of the woman she admired most, Lady Bexborough, opening the fête with the telegram in her hand.

There were so many books spread open, but none that seemed right to take to Evelyn Whitbread in hospital. There was nothing that would make that dried-up little woman look pleased, just for a moment, as Clarissa came in. How much she wanted people to look pleased as she came in, Clarissa thought. And she turned and walked back towards Bond Street, annoyed. For it was silly to have other reasons for doing things. She would much rather have been like Richard, who did things simply because he wanted to. Instead, she thought, waiting to cross the street, half the time she did things to make people think this or that.

Oh, if she could have had her life over again, she thought, stepping on to the pavement; if she could have even looked different! She would have been dark, like Lady Bexborough, with tough skin and beautiful eyes; slow and **splendid**, rather large, interested in politics like a man, very **sincere**. Instead, she had a narrow stick-like body and a silly little face, like a bird's, even if it was true that she carried herself well. But now this body that she wore, with all it could do, seemed nothing at all. She had the oddest feeling of being unseen, unknown; there would be no more marrying, no more having children now. There was only this extraordinary and rather solemn progress with the rest of them, up Bond Street; this being Mrs Dalloway, not even Clarissa any more; this being Mrs Richard Dalloway.

Bond Street fascinated her with its flags flying, its quiet

shops; nothing **extravagant** – there a roll of cloth where her father had bought his suits for fifty years; there some necklaces; there a fish on a bed of ice.

"That is all," she said, looking at the fish shop. "That is all," she repeated, pausing for a moment at the window of a glove shop where, before the War, you could buy almost perfect gloves. She took such pleasure in gloves; but her own daughter, Elizabeth, did not care for them one bit.

Not one bit, she thought, going up Bond Street to a shop where they kept flowers for her when she gave a party. Elizabeth really cared for her dog most of all. Still, that was better than sitting in an airless bedroom with Miss Kilman, praying! It might just be something, as Richard said, that all girls go through. It might be falling in love. But why with Miss Kilman? She had been badly treated during the war, of course, losing her job, and one **pitied** her for that. And Richard said she was very clever, had a great mind. But Elizabeth, her own daughter, was always with her. And Miss Kilman did not care a bit how she dressed or how she treated people who came to lunch. She cared greatly about the state of the Russians and the Austrians, but in private caused such pain, being so uncaring, dressed every day of the year in the same old green raincoat. She was never in the room for five minutes without making you feel how **superior** she was, how **inferior** you were; how poor she was, how rich you were. It was not really her that one hated, but the idea of her, which had probably turned into something that was not Miss Kilman, a monster to battle in the night. Maybe in another world she would have loved Miss Kilman. But not in this world. No!

It hurt her, though, to have this monster stirring within her, never to feel quite happy, quite safe. For at any moment the **hatred** would stir and had the **power**, especially since her influenza, to give her actual pain. It shook all pleasure in beauty, in friendship, in being well, in being loved, in making her home lovely, as if a monster were trying to dig it up by the **roots**. As if happiness were nothing but self-love!

Nonsense! she cried to herself, pushing through the doors of Mulberry's flower shop.

She advanced, light, tall, very upright, to be greeted by Miss Pym, whose hands were always bright red, as if they had been plunged in cold water with the flowers.

There were flowers of all colours: snowy white, palest blue, dark red, deep orange. She breathed in the earthy, garden-sweet smell as she stood talking to Miss Pym, who thought her kind. For Mrs Dalloway had been kind years ago, very kind, but she looked older this year, turning her head from side to side among the roses, smelling them with her eyes half-closed.

She went from jar to jar with Miss Pym, choosing. Nonsense, nonsense, she said to herself, more and more gently, as if this beauty, this smell, this colour, and Miss Pym liking her were a wave rolling over her, defeating that hatred and lifting her up, when – Oh! A gunshot in the street outside!

"Oh dear, those car engines!" said Miss Pym, going to the window to look, smiling and apologizing, as if the noise of those car engines were all *her* **fault**.

The violent explosion that made Mrs Dalloway jump came from a grey car which had stopped opposite Mulberry's window.

18

People outside on the pavement, who stopped and stared, had just enough time to see a face of the very greatest importance inside, against the pale grey cloth, before a hand pulled down a grey **blind**.

Word travelled quickly up and down Bond Street, like a silent mist, touching the street with its quiet, solemn mystery. But nobody knew whose face had been seen. Was it the Prince of Wales's, the Queen's, the Prime Minister's? Whose face was it? Nobody knew.

A man said, "The Prime Minister's car."

———————

Septimus Warren Smith, who found himself unable to move, heard the man speak.

Thirty, pale-faced, wearing brown shoes and an old coat, Septimus Warren Smith had that worried look in his brown eyes that makes complete strangers feel worried, too.

Everything on Bond Street had come to a stop; no traffic could get past the grey car outside Mulberry's. Mrs Dalloway, coming to the window with her arms full of flowers, looked out. Everyone looked at the car.

Septimus looked. There it stood, the blinds pulled down, and on them a strange pattern like a tree, Septimus thought. Watching in terror, everything slowly came together into one centre before his eyes, as if some horror was just below the **surface**, about to break through. It is I who am in the way, he thought. Wasn't he being looked at and pointed at? Wasn't he **rooted** to the pavement for a purpose? But for what purpose?

"Let us go on, Septimus," said his wife, a little Italian woman with large eyes in a pointed face.

But Rezia herself could not help looking at the car and its blinds pulled down. Was it the Queen in there, going shopping?

"Come on," said Rezia.

But her husband (for they had been married five years) jumped and said, "All right!" angrily, as if she had interrupted him.

People must notice, Rezia thought, looking at the crowd staring at the grey car. She admired English people with their children and their horses and their clothes, but they were just "people" now, because Septimus had said "I will kill myself". It was an awful thing to say. Suppose they had heard him? She looked at the crowd. Help, help! she wanted to cry out to the butcher's boys and the women. Help! Only last autumn she and Septimus had stood by the river wrapped in the same **cloak**, laughing. But one must hide failure. She must take him away into some park.

"Now we will cross," she said.

She had a right to his arm, though he gave it to her without feeling. What he gave her, though she was so young and simple, only twenty-four, without friends in England, and had left Italy for his **sake**, was only a piece of bone.

The car, with its blinds down, hiding a person of the greatest importance, perhaps the Queen, Prince or Prime Minister, advanced towards Piccadilly, solemn, mysterious.

It is probably the Queen, thought Mrs Dalloway, coming out of Mulberry's with her flowers. The Queen is going to visit some hospital; the Queen is going to open some church fête, thought Clarissa. Slowly and silently the car went on its way, carrying that very great person whom history would remember, to light a spark among Hugh Whitbread and the gentlemen of England, that night in Buckingham Palace. And Clarissa, too, was giving a party. She stood a little straighter, as if standing ready to greet her guests at the top of her stairs.

The car had gone, but it had caused a tiny wave, which rolled up Bond Street. For thirty seconds all heads were turned the same way and in all the hat shops and glove shops strangers looked at each other and thought of their King, their country, the dead.

A small crowd meanwhile had **gathered** at the gates of Buckingham Palace, poor people all of them, waiting to see the car. The Queen might pass by and look at them, or the Prince. The Prince might be coming along in the morning to visit his mother, Sarah Bletchley said, with her baby in her arms.

Suddenly, the sound of an aeroplane filled their ears. There it was coming over the trees, letting out white smoke behind it, writing something, making letters in the sky! Everyone looked up.

But what letters? Was it a C? An E, then an L? The letters moved and melted up in the sky. Then the aeroplane flew further away and, in a fresh space of sky, began writing a K, and E, a Y perhaps?

"*Glaxo*," someone said.

"*Kreemo*," said Sarah Bletchley.

At the gates of Buckingham Palace people looked up into the sky, and in this extraordinary silence and peace, bells **struck** eleven times, the sound fading up there among the birds.

The aeroplane turned and raced exactly where it liked.

"It says '**toffee**'," said a man, as the grey car went through the palace gates and nobody saw it.

Rezia Warren Smith, sitting by her husband's side on a seat in Regent's Park, looked up.

"Look, look, Septimus!" she cried. For Dr Holmes had told her to make her husband (who had nothing at all serious the matter with him but was not quite his usual self) take an interest in things outside himself.

So, thought Septimus, looking up, they are making signs to me. Not in actual words; that is, he could not read their language yet; but this beauty was clear enough. Tears filled his eyes as he looked at the words melting in the sky and presenting him, in their extraordinary goodness, one shape after another of incredible beauty. Tears ran down his cheeks.

They were advertising toffee, a woman told Rezia. Together they began to spell T . . .O . . .F . . .

"F . . .E . . .E," said the woman, and Septimus heard her rough voice close to his ear, which sent waves of sound running up to his brain. What a wonderful discovery, that the human voice could bring trees to life! Thankfully Rezia put her hand down heavily on his knee so that he was weighed down, or the sight of the trees rising and falling, rising and falling would have sent him mad. But he would not go mad. He would shut his eyes; he would see no more.

But the trees called to him; the leaves were alive; the trees were alive. And because they were connected with his body, when the branches stretched, he stretched, too. A child cried. Far away a dog **barked**.

"Septimus!" said Rezia, and he jumped violently. People would notice.

"I am going to walk to the fountain and back," she said.

For she could bear it no longer. Dr Holmes might say there was nothing at all serious the matter. She would rather he was dead! She could not sit beside him when he stared so hard and did not see her and made everything terrible. The sky and trees, children playing, dogs barking, all were terrible. And she could tell no one. "Septimus has been working too hard" was all she could say to her own mother. To love makes one alone, she thought. She could tell nobody, not even Septimus now. Looking back, she saw him sitting in his old coat, alone on the seat, bent forward, staring. And it was cowardly for a man to say he would kill himself. But Septimus had fought in the War; he was brave. He was not Septimus now. He never noticed her; he was happy without her. Nothing could make her happy without him. She looked down at her hand, spreading her fingers. Her wedding ring was loose because she had grown so thin. It was she who suffered, but she had nobody to tell.

Italy was far away, and the white houses, and the room where her sisters sat making hats, and the busy streets. In Milan the streets were crowded every evening with people walking, laughing, not half-alive, like people here, looking at a few ugly flowers!

"For you should see the gardens in Milan," she said aloud. But to whom?

There was nobody. Her words faded.

I am alone! she cried, by the fountain in Regent's Park. She was his wife, married years ago in Milan, and would never, never tell anyone that he was mad! She turned and there he was, still sitting alone in his old coat, staring, talking aloud.

Septimus listened to the voice which spoke to him, telling him he had come to save society. Men must not cut down trees. Change the world. No one kills from hatred. (He wrote such things down on the backs of envelopes.) He waited. He listened. A bird on the fence opposite sang, "Septimus, Septimus" four or five times, and then loud words in Greek about life beyond a river where the dead walk.

White things were gathering behind the fence. But he could not bear to look. Evans was behind the fence!

"What are you saying?" said Rezia suddenly, sitting down by him.

Interrupted again! She was always interrupting.

They must get away from people, he told her, jumping up. Over there, in the chairs beneath a tree. There they sat down under the tree.

"Look," she begged him, pointing at a group of little boys carrying **cricket** things. For Dr Holmes had told her to make him notice real things, go to the theatre, or play cricket – that was a nice game, just right for her husband.

"Look," she repeated.

Look, commanded the voice that told him he was the greatest of all men, taken from life to death to suffer forever. But he did not want it, he cried, with a wave of his hand.

"Oh, look," Rezia begged him, for he should not talk aloud to himself outdoors. But what was there to look at? A few sheep, that was all.

Could they tell her the way to Regent's Park Tube Station? Maisie Johnson wanted to know. She had only arrived from Edinburgh two days ago.

"Not this way – over there!" Rezia cried, waving her away, in case she saw Septimus.

Both of them seemed strange, Maisie Johnson thought. Everything seemed very strange. She was only nineteen and in London for the first time, to start a job at her uncle's business, and now, walking through Regent's Park, this couple on the chairs gave her quite a shock. She thought she would never forget it, even in fifty years' time. The young woman, jumping and waving her hands, seemed foreign; the man looked so awfully odd. Perhaps they were quarrelling. Perhaps they were parting for ever. Something was wrong, Maisie knew, and it had quite upset her.

Above her the aeroplane raced, away and away, until it was nothing but a bright spark. Then it rushed out over St Paul's Cathedral, strange and silent. Not a sound could be heard up there over the noise of the traffic. And now from behind the aeroplane, going up and up, straight up, in pure joy, poured white smoke, writing a T, an O, an F.

---

"What are people looking at, up in the sky?" Clarissa Dalloway asked Lucy, reaching her own front door and stepping inside.

The hall of the house was as cool as a church. The door closed, and Mrs Dalloway felt the life of her house wrap comfortably around her. Bending her head gratefully over the hall table, she took the note with the telephone message on it, while Lucy stood beside her, trying to explain.

"Mr Dalloway, madam –"

Clarissa read the note. "Lady Bruton wishes to know if Mr Dalloway will have lunch with her today."

"Mr Dalloway, madam, told me to tell you he would be having lunch out," said Lucy.

"Oh, dear!" said Clarissa, and Lucy shared her disappointment, and felt the understanding between them.

Clarissa **trembled**, for the shock of Lady Bruton asking Richard to lunch without her shook the moment. Millicent Bruton, whose lunch parties were said to be extraordinarily amusing, had not asked her. Simple jealousy could not separate her from Richard. But she feared time itself, and read on Lady Bruton's face, as if it had been cut in stone, the fading of her own life year by year.

She put down the note and began to go slowly upstairs, as if she had left a party and stood alone against the awful night, instead of against the stare of this soft June morning. She paused by the open window on the stairs. She felt herself suddenly older, dried-up, her body and brain now failed, because Lady Bruton, whose lunch parties were said to be extraordinarily amusing, had not asked her.

So, she went upstairs, paused at the window, came to her **attic** room. Here was an emptiness at the heart of life; an attic room. White sheets were stretched tight around the narrow bed. For Richard had to stay so late at the House of Commons that she must sleep undisturbed, he said, after her illness. So her room was an attic, and the bed narrow, with a book beside it.

She knew what was missing in her. It was something central,

something warm; a warm wave that broke up the cold contact of man and woman, or between women, too. She had a coldness about her which attached itself to her like a sheet. Yet there were times she did feel it, only for a moment, but it was enough; a sudden spark, which spread and rushed through her.

But this question of love, she thought, taking off her yellow hat and laying it on the bed, this falling in love with women, like Sally Seton. Had not that, after all, been love?

Sally sat on the floor – that was her first memory of Sally – smoking a cigarette. Where could it have been? At some party, she supposed, for Clarissa remembered the man she was with telling her who it was. He told her that Sally's parents did not **get on**. (How that shocked her – the idea that one's parents should quarrel!) But all that evening she could not take her eyes off Sally. It was an extraordinary beauty of the kind she most admired – dark, large-eyed, with that quality Clarissa wished she had herself – that she could say anything, do anything. Perhaps it was that summer that Sally came to stay at Bourton, rushing off after some argument at home, walking in quite unexpectedly one evening after dinner. It upset poor Aunt Helena so much that she never forgave her.

That night she and Sally had sat up half the night talking. It was Sally who made her feel, for the first time, how little she knew. She knew nothing about sex, nothing about social problems. That summer they sat, hour after hour, talking in her bedroom about life, about how they were going to change the world, though the ideas were Sally's, of course.

Sally's power was amazing. There was what she did with

flowers, for example. At Bourton there were always stiff little bunches all the way down the dinner table. But Sally picked all sorts of flowers from the garden that had never been seen together, cut their heads off, and made them swim on the top of water in bowls. The effect was extraordinary. Then one night she forgot her towel and ran along the corridor naked, shocking Aunt Helena. Indeed, she did shock people.

The strange thing, looking back, was how pure her feeling for Sally was. It was not like one's feeling for a man. She could remember standing in her bedroom, saying aloud, "She is beneath this roof!"

The words meant nothing at all to her now. But she could remember going cold with excitement, doing her hair (and now the old feeling began to come back to her, as she put her hand up to her hair). It was a feeling of pure joy, coming down to dinner in a white dress to meet Sally Seton, who seemed all light.

After dinner, Aunt Helena wandered off. Sally stood by the window talking in her beautiful voice to Papa, who had begun to be attracted to her without intending to be. (He never forgot lending her one of his books and finding that she had left it out in the rain.) Peter Walsh was there, and old Joseph Breitkopf, who came every summer to teach Clarissa German. Suddenly Sally said, "What a pity to sit indoors!" and they went out into the garden. Peter and Joseph Breitkopf talked about German music. She and Sally walked a little behind them. Then came the most beautiful moment of her whole life. Passing a stone pot with flowers in it, Sally stopped, picked a flower, kissed her on the lips. The whole world seemed to have turned **upside down**.

The others disappeared; she was alone with Sally. And she felt that she had been given some extraordinary treasure, like a diamond, and told just to keep it, not to look at it. Then old Joseph and Peter turned to face them.

"Star-**gazing**?" said Peter.

It was shocking; it was horrible! It was like running into a stone wall in the darkness! But she did not mind for herself; she felt only how Sally was being attacked. She saw Peter's jealousy, his wish to break into their friendship. But Sally continued on her way, undefeated. She made old Joseph tell her the names of the stars. Never had she admired Sally so much!

She stood there. She listened to Joseph telling Sally the names of the stars.

"Oh, this horror!" she said to herself, as if she had known all the time that something would interrupt her moment of happiness.

When she thought of Peter, she always thought of their **quarrels** – because she wanted him to think well of her, perhaps. Yet how much she owed Peter later. He gave her words that guarded her life, like "**sentimental**". A book was sentimental; an opinion was sentimental. Perhaps she was sentimental now to be thinking of the past. What would he think, she wondered, when he came back? Would he think that she had grown older? Would he say that, or would she see him thinking it? It was true. Since her illness her hair had turned almost white.

Sitting at her table, in front of the mirror, an icy shock went through her. She was not old yet. She had just passed her fifty-first birthday. Months and months of her fifty-second year were still untouched. And, as if to catch the falling moment, Clarissa plunged into the very heart of it – the moment of this June morning – as she gazed into the small pink face of the woman who was to give a party that very night; of Clarissa Dalloway; of herself.

How many million times she had seen her face in the mirror, always with the same tightness of her lips. That was her self – pointed, like an arrow, and certain. That was her self when, with effort, she gathered the parts together into one centre, one woman who was there for others. She had helped the lonely, perhaps; and young people, who were grateful to her. She had tried always to be the same, never showing a sign of all the other sides of her – of her failings, doubts, and jealousies, like this of Lady Bruton not asking her to lunch. (She brushed her hair at last.) Now where was her dress?

Her evening dresses hung in the cupboard. Clarissa, plunging her hand into the softness, gently took out the silvery-green dress and carried it to the window to examine it. She had torn it. She remembered someone stepping on the skirt at a party. She would mend it herself. Her servants had too much to do. She would take it downstairs to the **drawing room** and sew it there, for she needed to check that all was well for the party.

It was strange, she thought, pausing at the top of the stairs, how well a woman knows the mood of her house. Quiet, purposeful sounds reached her from downstairs: a brush moving across the floor, voices repeating messages, clean silver bowls and **candlesticks** being carried on a tray. All was for the party.

And Lucy went into the drawing room with her tray, and put

the huge silver candlesticks on the table. Here the guests would later stand and talk, she thought. And of all those people, her Mrs Dalloway was the loveliest.

"Oh Lucy," said Mrs Dalloway, coming into the drawing room, "the silver does look nice!"

And Lucy stopped at the drawing room door and said very shyly, Couldn't she help to mend that dress?

But, said Mrs Dalloway, Lucy had more than enough work to do already, without that.

"But thank you, Lucy, oh, thank you," said Mrs Dalloway. And thank you, thank you, she went on saying (sitting down on the sofa with the green dress over her knees), grateful to her servants for helping her to be what she wanted: gentle, generous-hearted. Her servants liked her. Now where was the dress torn?

Quiet fell on her as she sewed, gathering the folds of silk smoothly together. So on a summer's day, the waves gather, rise and fall; rise and fall; and the whole world seems to be saying "that is all". That is all, the heart repeats. *Fear no more*. And the body alone listens to the wave breaking, the dog barking, far away, barking and barking.

"**Good heavens**, the front-door bell!" cried Clarissa, looking up. She listened.

"Mrs Dalloway will see me," said the grey-haired man in the hall. "Oh yes, after I've been in India for five years, Clarissa will see *me*," he said, putting Lucy **aside** very kindly and running upstairs.

"Who can it be?" asked Mrs Dalloway (how shocking it was to be interrupted at eleven o'clock in the morning, on the day she

31

was giving a party). She wanted to hide her sewing. Now the door opened, and in came – For a second she could not remember what he was called, being so shocked, so pleased, to have Peter Walsh come to visit her without warning!

"And how are you?" said Peter Walsh, trembling, taking both her hands and kissing them. She's grown older, he thought, sitting down beside her. I shan't tell her, though. She's looking at me, he thought, feeling suddenly embarrassed. He took out a pocket-knife and half-opened it.

He's exactly the same, thought Clarissa; he has the same odd look, the same clothes. He's a little thinner, and dryer, perhaps, but he looks awfully well, and just the same as he used to.

"How heavenly it is to see you again!" she cried. He had his knife out. That's so like him, she thought.

He had only arrived in London last night, he said. And how was everything, how was everybody – Richard? Elizabeth?

"And what's all this?" he said, pointing his knife towards her evening dress.

He's very well dressed, thought Clarissa; yet he always **criticizes** *me*.

Here she is, mending her dress as usual, he thought. All the time I've been working in India she's been sitting here, going to parties, running to the House of Commons and back for Richard. For there's nothing in the world so bad for some women as marriage, and having a husband in politics, he thought, growing more and more annoyed.

"Richard's very well. He's at a government meeting," said Clarissa.

And she picked up her sewing and asked did he mind her just finishing what she was doing, for they had a party that night?

"Which I shan't ask you to," she said. "My dear Peter!" she said.

But it was wonderful to hear her say that – my dear Peter! Indeed, it was all so wonderful – the house, the silver candlesticks, the paintings!

Why wouldn't she ask him to her party? he asked.

Now he's perfectly charming, of course, thought Clarissa. Now I remember how impossible it was to decide. And why did I decide not to marry him, that awful summer?

"But it's so extraordinary that you should have come this morning!" she cried. "Do you remember," she said, "the French windows at Bourton?"

"I do," he said, and he remembered having breakfast alone, very awkwardly, with her father, (who had recently died, and he had not written to her about it). But he had never got on well with old Justin Parry, Clarissa's father.

"I often wish I'd got on better with your father," he said.

"But he never liked anyone who wanted – liked my friends," said Clarissa, cross with herself for reminding Peter that he had wanted to marry her.

Of course I wanted to, thought Peter, and was **overcome** with his own sadness, which rose like a pale moon above a garden. It almost broke my heart, too, he thought. I was more unhappy than I have ever been since. And, as if he were really sitting in the garden at Bourton with Clarissa, he moved a little towards her, raised his hand, let it fall. She seemed to be sitting with him in the moonlight.

"Herbert has Bourton now," she said. "I never go there now."

Then, just like in a moonlit garden, when one person feels embarrassed that he is already bored, while the other still looks sadly at the moon, so Peter Walsh felt now. He moved his foot, looked at the furniture, said nothing. For why go back to the past like this? Why make him suffer?

"Do you remember the lake?" she said suddenly, her voice full of an **emotion** which caught her heart and made her throat stiff. For she was a child, throwing bread to the ducks, standing between her parents. At the same time she was a grown woman, coming to her parents by the lake, saying, "This is what I've made of my life!" And what had she made of it, sitting there sewing this morning with Peter?

She looked at Peter Walsh through tears and dried her eyes.

"Yes," said Peter. "Yes, yes, yes," he said, as if she were bringing something to the surface which hurt him as it rose. Stop! he wanted to cry. For he was not old; his life was not over; not at all. He was only just past fifty. Shall I tell her my news, he thought. But she is too cold, sitting there sewing, he thought. Daisy would look ordinary beside Clarissa. And she would think me a failure, which I am in the Dalloways' eyes, he thought. Oh yes, he was a failure compared with all this – the beautiful furniture and the silver and the old English paintings! I hate it, he thought, and this has been going on all the time, week after week, while I – And at once his life seemed to spread out before him: journeys, quarrels, adventures, relationships with women, and work, work, work! He wrapped his fingers around his knife.

What an extraordinary habit that was, Clarissa thought, always playing with a knife, always making one feel silly, shallow, empty-minded. But, like a queen whose guards have fallen asleep and left her unprotected, she commanded her feelings for the things and people she loved to come to her aid. She commanded them all – her life, which Peter hardly knew now – to come and beat off the enemy.

"Well, and what's happened to you?" she said, challenging Peter to the battle. He gathered together all sorts of things: his marriage, which she knew nothing at all about; his relationships; his work in India.

"Millions and millions of things!" he cried.

Clarissa sat very upright.

"I am in love," he said, as if about to lay down flowers before her in the dark.

"In love with a girl in India," he said, now speaking rather dryly to Clarissa Dalloway. He had laid down his flowers. Clarissa would make her judgement.

"In love!" she said. How could he be dragged under by that monster at his age? His neck is thin, his hands are red, and he is older than me! But in her heart she felt, he is in love.

She sat with her dress on her knee, trembling a little. He was in love! Not with her. With some younger woman, of course.

"And who is she?" she asked.

"A married woman, unfortunately," he said. "The wife of an officer in the Indian Army."

And he smiled as he placed Daisy before Clarissa in this **foolish** way.

(All the same, he is in love, thought Clarissa.)

"She has," he continued, "two small children; a boy and a girl; and I have come over to see my lawyers about the divorce."

There they are, Daisy and her children, he thought. Do what you like with them, Clarissa! And with each passing second it seemed to him that his Daisy and her two small children became more and more lovely as Clarissa looked at them.

The woman must make him feel important, thought Clarissa. Peter had been fooled like that all his life, first marrying a girl he met on the boat out to India, now wanting to marry the wife of an officer in the Indian Army. Thank Heaven she had refused to marry him! Still, her old friend, her dear Peter, was in love.

"But what are you going to do?" she asked him.

Oh, some lawyers called Hooper and Grateley were going to arrange it, he said. And he actually cut his fingernails with his knife.

Oh, leave your knife alone! she cried to herself. It had always annoyed her that he did not have the least idea what anyone else was feeling; and now, at his age, how silly!

I know who I am up against, thought Peter, running his finger against his knife – Clarissa and Richard Dalloway, and all the rest of them. But I'll show Clarissa. And then, to his complete surprise, he began to cry, sitting beside her on the sofa, the tears running down his cheeks.

And Clarissa had leaned forward, taken his hand, gathered him to her, kissed him. She had actually felt his face on hers before she could control the emotion which rose, then fell, leaving her holding his hand. She felt, as she sat back, extraordinarily light-hearted. And all of a sudden it came over her – if I had married him, this joy would have been mine all day!

It was all over for her. The sheet was stretched and the bed was narrow. Richard, Richard! she cried, calling to him to protect her, as a sleeper in the night wakes and reaches out a hand in the dark. He is lunching with Lady Bruton, she remembered. He has left me; I am alone for ever, she thought, folding her hands on her knee.

Peter Walsh had gone to the window and stood with his back to her, blowing his nose, his thin shoulders lifting slightly. Take me with you, thought Clarissa suddenly, as if he were about to leave on some great journey. And then, the next moment, it was as if an exciting play had finished. She had lived a lifetime in it – had run away, had lived with Peter, and now it was over. It was time to move. And, as a woman gathers her cloak, her gloves, her bag, and gets up to go out of the theatre into the street, she rose from the sofa and went to Peter.

And it was awfully strange, he thought, how she still had the power to make the moon, which he hated, rise over the garden at Bourton.

"Tell me," he said, taking her by the shoulders. "Are you happy, Clarissa? Does Richard –"

The door opened.

"Here is my Elizabeth," said Clarissa, emotionally, extravagantly, perhaps.

"How do you do?" said Elizabeth, coming forward.

The sound of Big Ben **striking** the half-hour rang out between them with extraordinary force.

"Hello, Elizabeth!" cried Peter, saying "Goodbye, Clarissa" without looking at her, leaving the room quickly, running downstairs and opening the front door.

"Peter! Peter!" cried Clarissa, following him to the top of the stairs. "My party tonight! Remember my party tonight!" she cried over the noise of the traffic and all the clocks striking. And as Peter Walsh shut the front door, her voice crying "Remember my party tonight!" sounded very far away.

———————

Remember my party, remember my party, said Peter Walsh as he stepped down the street, speaking to himself in time with the echo of Big Ben. (It was still early; only half-past eleven.) Oh, Clarissa's parties, he thought. Why does she give these parties? Not that he blamed her. Only one person in the world could be as he was: in love. And there he was, this fortunate man, reflected in a shop window, all India behind him, really in love for the first time in his life.

Clarissa had grown hard, he thought, and a little sentimental. The way she said, "Here is my Elizabeth!" annoyed him. Why not just "Here's Elizabeth?" It was **insincere**. And Elizabeth didn't like it either. For he understood young people; he liked them. There was always something cold in Clarissa, he thought. She had always had, even as a girl, a kind of shyness, which in middle age becomes ordinariness, and then it's all over, he thought. Had he annoyed her by visiting at that time? he wondered. Then he felt suddenly embarrassed at having been such a fool, crying, telling her everything, as usual.

As a cloud crosses the sun, silence falls on London, and falls on the mind. There we stop; there we stand. It is only habit that keeps us going, Peter Walsh said to himself, pausing, feeling empty inside. He stood there thinking, Clarissa refused me.

The bells of St Margaret's church rang out two minutes late, as usual. Clarissa has been ill, he thought. It was her heart, he remembered. And as the final bell suddenly rang out, loud and solemn, for death that surprised in the middle of life, he thought of Clarissa falling where she stood. No! No! he cried. She is not dead! I am not old, he cried, marching up Whitehall, as if his future stretched before him there, forceful, unending.

He was not old, or fixed, or dried-up in the least. He did not care a bit what the Dalloways and the Whitbreads and their sort of people said about him. True, he had not finished his studies at Oxford University, he had rejected their kind of politics, he had failed in some ways. But the future lies in the hands of young men like himself, as he had been thirty years ago, with their love of ideas, always reading, reading science, reading philosophy.

A noise came from behind, a regular, **thudding** sound. Boys in uniform, carrying guns, marched with their eyes ahead of them, their arms stiff, on their solemn progress away from the Cenotaph. They reached him, marched on past him to Trafalgar Square and disappeared.

Nobody yet knew he was in London, except Clarissa. And the strangeness of standing alone, alive, unknown, at half-past eleven in Trafalgar Square flooded over him. His mind emptied and he

39

felt a sudden, powerful joy. He had escaped! He was completely free. I haven't felt so young for years! thought Peter, feeling like a child who runs outdoors.

A young woman in a long cloak came walking across Trafalgar Square. She's extraordinarily beautiful, Peter thought, starting to follow her. Even with her back turned, she seemed to choose him. "You," she said, with her white gloves and her long thin cloak, which blew out a little in the wind, like open arms that would offer **comfort**.

She waited at the edge of the pavement. She was not rich, like Clarissa, but there was a **dignity** about her. She crossed the road; he followed. The last thing he wanted was to make her embarrassed. But if she stopped he would say, "Come and have an ice cream" and she would answer simply, "Oh yes."

Other people came between them. He kept following; he was a wild, romantic adventurer. On and on she went, across Piccadilly Circus, up Regent Street, across Oxford Street, turning down one of the little side streets. Finally, she stopped at a house, opened her bag, and with one look in his direction, but not at him, put her key in the door and was gone. It was over!

Well, I've had my fun, he thought. It was over, and half-imagined, as he knew very well. He had invented it, invented her; as one invents most of life, he thought. Clarissa's voice sang in his ears, Remember my party, remember my party.

He turned and went up the street, thinking he would find somewhere to sit, till it was time for the lawyers. Where should he go? It didn't matter, he thought, for it was still very early. Up the street then, towards Regent's Park. It was a splendid morning, too, and London was a splendid achievement in its way. The doctors, office workers and purposeful women, all going about their business, seemed to him wholly admirable and good.

He had walked in Regent's Park as a child. It is odd, he thought, how the past keeps coming back to me – the result of seeing Clarissa, perhaps. For women live much more in the past than we do, he thought, and attach themselves to places.

Here he was in Regent's Park and yes, he remembered it. He would find an empty seat in the shade and smoke. He did not want to be disturbed by people asking him the time. There was a long seat with an old grey-haired **nanny**, and a baby asleep in a pram beside her; he would sit at the far end of that seat.

She's an odd-looking girl, he thought, suddenly remembering Elizabeth coming into the room and standing by her mother. She's quite grown up now, no more than eighteen, and handsome rather than pretty. She probably doesn't get on with Clarissa. I shall try and speak with Elizabeth alone tonight, he thought. He watched the smoke from his cigarette slowly making odd shapes in the air and gradually fading away. Suddenly he closed his eyes, raised his hand with great effort, and threw away the heavy end of his cigarette. His mind emptied, shutting out the children's voices, people passing, rising and falling traffic. Down, down he fell into sleep, while beside him on the hot seat the old nanny watched over the baby sleeping in its pram, and the baby's little sister playing on the grass.

Peter Walsh woke suddenly. "Good heavens!" he said to himself out loud. He had been dreaming of some scene, some room, some past, which gradually became clearer.

It was at Bourton that summer, when he was so much in love with Clarissa. There were a lot of people there, sitting round a table, talking and laughing. He remembered Sally Seton, Clarissa's dearest friend, who was always at Bourton. (He gave Sally cigarettes, which she smoked in her bedroom, and Clarissa's father disliked them both equally, which made them great friends.) He remembered a terrible quarrel with Clarissa about a neighbour who had married a woman who had once been his servant. Did they know that the wife had had a baby before they were married, Sally Seton said. Clarissa had been greatly offended – she would never speak to the woman again! Peter did not blame her for minding – girls brought up in the way she had been knew nothing. It was her manner that annoyed him: hard, cold, superior. She knew that he criticized her, even without speaking. She got up and went off alone.

As soon as she shut the door he felt deeply unhappy. It all seemed useless – going on being in love, going on quarrelling, going on forgiving each other and being friends again. It was an awful evening! And he couldn't speak to her about it – there were always people about and she carried on as if nothing had happened. That was the worst part of her – this coldness, this woodenness, which he had felt again this morning. Yet Heaven knows he loved her.

He had gone into dinner late and sat down by Aunt Helena – old Miss Parry – a fierce old lady, but who was kind to him. And then halfway through dinner he made himself look across at Clarissa for the first time. She was talking to a young man on her right, and he suddenly said to himself, "She will marry that man." He didn't even know the man's name.

For it was that afternoon, of course, that Richard Dalloway had come to Bourton.

Later, Clarissa had come up to him, with her perfect manners, and spoken to him as if they had never met before, which made him angry. "The perfect hostess," he said to her, and saw how it hurt her. But he meant to hurt her, after seeing her with Dalloway. Then she left him, and he had a feeling that they were all gathered together against him, laughing and talking behind his back. He stood by Aunt Helena, talking about wild flowers. Never had he suffered so much! People began going out of the room. He heard them talking about fetching cloaks, because it was cold on the water. They were going boating on the lake by moonlight – one of Sally's mad ideas. And they all went out. He was left quite alone.

"Don't you want to go with them?" said Aunt Helena. She had guessed. And he turned round and there was Clarissa again. She had come back to fetch him. He was overcome by her goodness.

"Come along," Clarissa said. "They're waiting."

They walked down to the lake. He had never felt so happy in the whole of his life! Without even speaking, they were friends again. He had twenty minutes of perfect happiness. And all the time he knew perfectly well that Dalloway was falling in love with her, that she was falling in love with Dalloway; but it didn't seem to matter. Nothing mattered. They sat on the ground and talked. They went in and out of each other's minds without any effort. And then in a second it was over. He said to himself as they were getting into the boat, "She will marry that man."

He knew that he was foolish. He asked impossible things of Clarissa. He made terrible scenes. She would have accepted him, perhaps, if he had been less foolish. Sally thought so.

It was an extraordinary summer – the awkward conversations with Clarissa's father, Justin Parry, at breakfast; Aunt Helena being fierce but kind; Sally taking him off for talks in the vegetable garden; Clarissa in bed with headaches.

The final terrible scene, which he believed mattered more than anything in the whole of his life, happened at three o'clock in the afternoon of a very hot day. It had started at lunch when Sally made a silly joke about Dalloway, and Clarissa was suddenly annoyed. That was all, but it was exactly as if she had said to him, "I'm only amusing myself with you; I have an understanding with Richard Dalloway."

He had not slept for nights. "It's got to be finished one way or the other," he said to himself. He sent a note to Clarissa by Sally, asking her to meet him by the fountain at three. "Something very important has happened," he wrote at the end of it.

She came early, and they stood with the fountain between them. She did not move.

"Tell me the truth," he kept on saying. He felt as if his head would explode. She seemed turned to stone. "Tell me the truth," he repeated. She was like iron, like hard stone. And when she said, "This is the end" – after he had spoken for a long while, with tears running down his cheeks – it was as if she had hit him. She turned, she left him, she went away.

"Clarissa!" he cried. "Clarissa!" But she never came back. It was over. He went away that night and never returned.

It was awful, he cried, awful, awful!

Still, the sun was hot. Still, one got over things. Still, life had a way of adding day to day, he thought, yawning and beginning to take notice of Regent's Park in the sunshine. The little girl who had been showing pretty stones to her old nanny at the other end of the seat ran off straight into a lady's legs. Peter Walsh laughed out loud.

———————

But as she walked down the wide path Rezia Warren Smith was saying to herself, Why should I suffer? She had left Septimus (who wasn't Septimus any longer), talking to himself, saying hard, cruel things, talking to a dead man. No, I can't bear it any longer, she was saying, when the little girl ran into her, fell down and began to cry.

That was strangely comforting. She stood the little girl upright, brushed the dirt from her dress and kissed her.

But she had done nothing wrong herself. She had loved Septimus; she had been happy; she had had a beautiful home in Milan, and her sisters still lived there, making hats. Why should *she* suffer?

The little girl ran straight back to her nanny. Rezia saw the kind-looking man next to them give her his watch to look at to comfort her.

But why should she suffer? Why hadn't she been left in Milan? Why?

Through her tears, the wide path, the nanny, the man in grey, the pram, all rose and fell before her eyes.

She must go back to Septimus since it was almost time for them to go to Sir William Bradshaw. She must go back to him sitting there on the green chair under the tree, talking to himself or to that dead man Evans, whom she had only seen once for a moment in Milan. He had seemed a nice, quiet man; a great friend of Septimus's, and he had been killed in the War. But such things happen to everyone. Everyone has friends who were killed in the War. Everyone gives up something when they marry. She had given up her home. She had come to live here, in this awful city. But Septimus let himself think about horrible things; and she could, too, if she tried. He had got stranger and stranger. He said people were talking behind the bedroom walls. He saw things, too – he had seen an old woman's head in the middle of a plant. He explained how evil people were, how he could see them inventing lies as they passed in the street. He knew all their thoughts, he said; he knew everything. He knew the meaning of the world, he said.

Yet he could be happy when he chose. They had been to Hampton Court Palace on an open-top bus, and they were perfectly happy. He had talked and laughed and chatted. But suddenly he had said, "Now we will kill ourselves," when they were standing by the river. He had looked at the river with a look she had also seen in his eyes when a train went by. She felt he was going from her and she caught him by the arm.

When they got home he could hardly walk. He lay on the sofa and made her hold his hand to prevent him from falling down, down, he cried, into the fire! He saw faces laughing at him, calling him horrible names, and hands pointing. He began to talk aloud, answering people, arguing, laughing, crying, getting very excited and making her write things down. It was all nonsense, about death, about Miss Isabel Pole, who had taught him Shakespeare.

She was near him now; she could see him gazing at the sky, whispering. Yet Dr Holmes said there was nothing the matter with him. What had happened then? Why did he jump when she sat down next to him, and point at her hand, looking terrified?

Was it because she had taken off her wedding ring? "My hand has grown so thin," she said. "I have put the ring in my purse."

He dropped her hand. Their marriage was over, he thought, with pain, and **relief**. He was free. He was alone. He, Septimus, had been called to hear the truth. Voices above his head spoke to him. Red flowers grew through his body. He felt that he was lying on a rock in the middle of the sea. I leaned over the edge of the boat and fell down, under the sea, he thought. I have been dead, but now I am alive. But let me rest, he begged. (He was talking to himself again – it was awful, awful!) And as a sleeper feels himself pulled to the shore of life when he wakes, so he felt himself pulled towards life. The sun became hotter, cries sounded louder.

He just had to open his eyes, but a weight was on them, a fear. He pushed; he looked; he saw Regent's Park in front of him. Sunlight fell at his feet, trees waved, birds flew round and round. Beauty was everywhere.

"It is time," said Rezia.

The word "time" cracked open. Words fell from his lips without him making them. He sang, and Evans answered from behind the tree. The dead were in Greece, Evans sang, among the flowers. They had been waiting there till the War was over, and now the dead, now Evans himself –

"No, don't come!" Septimus cried out. For he could not look at the dead.

But the branches parted. A man in grey was actually walking towards them. It was Evans! But there was no mud on him, no wounds; he was not changed. I must tell the whole world, Septimus cried, (as the dead man in the grey suit came nearer), getting up from his chair.

"The time, Septimus," Rezia repeated, trying to make him sit down. "What is the time?"

This man in the grey suit must have noticed them. He was looking at them.

"I will tell you the time," said Septimus, very slowly, very strangely. As he sat smiling at the dead man in the grey suit, a clock struck quarter to twelve.

––––––––––

And that is being young, Peter Walsh thought as he passed them – to have an awful scene in the middle of the morning. The poor girl looked very upset. But what was it about, he wondered. What had the young man been saying to make her look like that? What awful quarrel had they had, to both look so unhappy on a fine summer morning? The **fascinating** thing about coming back to England, after five years, was the way it made one notice things as if one had never seen them before, like those lovers quarrelling under a tree. He had never seen London look so beautiful – the softness, the richness, the greenness, he thought, after India. And here, of course, one fell in love with every woman one met. There was a freshness about them and all of them, even the poorest, were better dressed than five years ago, surely. And every woman now, even the finest, wore make-up, and put it on in public. And young women would marry when it suited them; they would marry some rich man and live in a huge house near Manchester.

Now who was it who had done that? Peter asked himself, walking across the grass. Somebody who had written him a long letter quite recently, who had been thinking of him and the old days. It was Sally Seton, of course! Wild, romantic Sally − the last person in the world one would have expected to marry a rich man and live in a huge house near Manchester.

But of all Clarissa's circle Sally was probably the best. At least she was not fooled by men like Hugh Whitbread, who was the greatest **snob** and who had the most stupid admiration for the British **upper-class** of any human being Peter had ever met. Hugh was like a top-class servant − somebody who walked behind his employer carrying luggage, who could be trusted to send telegrams or to write letters for hostesses. He had some silly little job now, looking after the King's wine, or cleaning royal buttons.

"And who are the Whitbreads?" he could hear Sally saying. "They sell coal." Hugh thought of nothing but his own appearance and **stood for** everything worst in British **middle-class** life, she said. Oh, but he was such a dear, so unselfish, giving up his own pleasure to help his old mother, Clarissa would say.

And now, Peter thought, if he married Daisy and brought her to England, he would need Hugh Whitbread or Richard

Dalloway to help get him a job with a good salary. He didn't mind asking Dalloway, who was a straightforward, sensible kind of man; not brilliant, and without a spark of imagination, but a good man. He ought to have been a country gentleman. He was wasted in politics. How good he had been when Clarissa's dog injured its leg so badly. Dalloway took care of it all, comforting Clarissa, and all the time talking to the dog as if it were a human being.

He remembered walking with Sally in the garden at Bourton, with its rose bushes and giant cauliflowers and Sally begging him, half laughing of course, to carry off Clarissa. He must save her from the Hugh Whitbreads and the Richard Dalloways and all the other perfect gentlemen who would take away her spark and make a hostess of her.

But one must be fair to Clarissa. She had a perfectly clear idea of what she wanted. Her emotions were all on the surface. Beneath, she was a far better judge of character than Sally, for example, and she had, too, that extraordinary woman's gift of making a world of her own wherever she was. In a roomful of people, it was Clarissa one remembered. Not that she was beautiful, or said anything especially clever. But there she was.

No, no, no! He was not in love with her any more! He only felt unable to get away from the thought of her, after seeing her that morning, which was not being in love, of course. It was simply thinking of her, criticizing her, trying again to explain her after thirty years. The obvious thing to say about her was that she cared too much for her position in society. She had admitted it to him and told him that she hated people who didn't try – failures, like himself, he supposed. She thought that people must do something, be something. She once said that the older she became, the more she admired the courage of a woman like Lady Bexborough, who held herself upright. (Clarissa did that herself, being as straight as an arrow, a little stiff in fact.) In all of this she was guided by Dalloway, of course. She had to see things through her husband's eyes. These parties, for example, were all for him. She made her drawing room a sort of meeting place. She had a gift for it: visiting, being kind to people, running about with bunches of flowers, but she did it sincerely. Since the whole of life is a bad joke, she used to say, let us at least do what we can to reduce the suffering of others and be as good as we possibly can. It was immediately after Sylvia's death, that terrible **tragedy**, that she developed these ideas. To see your own sister killed by a falling tree (which was all the fault of her father's carelessness), was enough to make one bitter, Clarissa always said. Instead, she developed this belief in doing good for the sake of goodness.

And of course she enjoyed life enormously. If you walked with her in the park, she would notice the flowers, a baby in a pram, the young couples (she would probably have talked to those lovers, if she had thought them unhappy). But she always needed people and as a result she wasted her time, always giving parties, talking nonsense.

There was a reward to getting old, Peter Walsh thought, coming out of Regent's Park. While emotions remain as strong as ever, one has gained, at last, the ability to hold experience up to the light and turn it round slowly to examine it.

Now, at the age of fifty-three, he hardly needed people any more. For hours at a time (he prayed that one could say these things without them being known!), for hours and days he never thought of Daisy. So was he really in love? The truth was that *she* was in love with *him*. And when the ship actually sailed from India he felt an extraordinary relief at being alone. If they were honest, Peter Walsh thought, everyone would say that one doesn't want people after fifty.

But what about these extraordinary states of emotion – crying this morning? Clarissa probably thought him a fool, not for the first time. It was jealousy that was at the bottom of it – jealousy which lasts longer than every other emotion, Peter Walsh thought, taking out his knife. In her last letter, Daisy mentioned another man. Even knowing that she said it on purpose, to make him jealous, made no difference to his wild jealousy. Coming to England and seeing lawyers wasn't because he wanted to marry her, but to prevent her marrying anybody else. That was what had come over him when he saw Clarissa so calm, so cold, sewing her dress. That was what she could have saved him from. She had turned him into a tearful old fool. But women don't know what love is, he thought, shutting his knife. Clarissa was as cold as ice. She would sit there on the sofa by his side, let him take her hand, give him one kiss – Here he was at the street crossing.

A sound interrupted him: a weak, thin, trembling sound, coming from just opposite Regent's Park Tube Station; an ageless, sexless voice, with no beginning or end, and an absence of all human meaning, singing:

*ee um fah um so*
*foo swee too eem oo . . .*

The beaten, bent old woman, with one hand held out for coins, the other holding her side, stood singing of love. She sang of a love which has lasted ten million years, of once walking in May with a man who had loved her.

"Give me your hand," she said, (for Peter Walsh couldn't help giving the poor creature a coin as he stepped into his taxi), "*and if someone sees, what do they matter?*" her trembling voice demanded.

---

"Poor old woman," said Rezia Warren Smith, waiting to cross the street.

Oh, poor old creature. Suppose it was a wet night? Where did she sleep at night? And suppose someone passed, like one's father, or someone who had known one in better days?

The thin sound of her singing rose up into the air like smoke, almost cheerfully. "*And if someone sees, what do they matter?*"

Since she had been so unhappy, for weeks and weeks now, Rezia had given meanings to things that happened. Sometimes she almost felt that she must stop people in the street, if they looked kind, to tell them "I am unhappy". And the words of this old woman singing in the street made her suddenly quite sure that everything was going to be all right. They were going to Sir William Bradshaw. She thought his name sounded nice; he would make Septimus better at once.

So they crossed the street, Mr and Mrs Septimus Warren Smith, and was there anything to bring attention to them after all? Was there anything to make people think here is a young man who carries in him the greatest message in the world, who is the happiest man in the world, and the unhappiest? Perhaps they walked more slowly than other people; there was something uncertain in the man's walk. But what was more natural for an office worker, (who has not been in the West End on a weekday at this time for years), than to keep looking around him, at the sky, at everything wonderful and strange?

He looked like an office worker, but of the better, educated sort. He wore brown boots, his hands were smooth, his face was intelligent, sensitive. He was one of those self-educated men who has borrowed books from libraries, and read them in the evening after work.

He had left home when he was still a boy because of his mother and because he could see no future for a poet in his country town. And so, telling only his little sister, he had gone to London, leaving a note behind him.

London has swallowed up many millions of men called Smith, not caring about extraordinary first names like Septimus. He became shy and nervous, determined to improve himself, and fell in love with Miss Isabel Pole, who gave talks about Shakespeare.

She lent him books, wrote him notes and lit in him the kind of fire that burns only once in a lifetime, without heat. He thought her beautiful and wise. He dreamed of her, wrote poems to her, threw them away. He finished a great work at three o'clock in the morning and ran out to the streets.

Mr Brewer, his boss, knew that something was wrong. He

thought highly of young Smith and expected that he would do well, if he kept his health. So he advised him to play football and invited him to supper. Mr Brewer was about to raise his salary when something interrupted his plans and took away his best young men – the War.

Septimus was one of the first to sign up to the army. He went to France to fight for his country, to save an England which for him meant Shakespeare's plays and Miss Isabel Pole in a green dress. In the War he gained what Mr Brewer thought he was missing – strength and manliness. He was noticed by his officer, Evans. The two of them were always together, sharing, fighting, quarrelling with each other. But when Evans was killed in Italy, just before the end, in autumn 1918, Septimus congratulated himself for feeling very little. The War had taught him. It was wonderful. He had gone through the whole thing and had survived. When peace came he was in Milan, staying in the house of an innkeeper, with little tables outside, flowers in pots and daughters making hats. He became engaged to Rezia, the younger daughter, one evening when, in terror, he realized that he could not feel.

For now that it was all over, the peace agreement signed and the dead buried, he had these sudden moments of fear. He could not feel. As he looked into the room where the daughters sat making hats, he could see them, he could hear them, but he could not feel. He stayed among them, listening to their work, their laughter, and felt protected. But when he woke alone early in the morning, the bed was falling, he was falling.

So he married Rezia, with her little artist's fingers.

"It's a lady's hat that matters most," she would say, when they walked out together. She would examine every hat that passed.

"Beautiful!" she would whisper, making Septimus look, too. But beauty was behind glass to him. He could not taste, he could not feel. His brain was perfect – he could read, he could calculate. So it must be the fault of the world then, that he could not feel.

It might be possible, Septimus thought, looking at England from the train window, after they had crossed the sea, that the world itself is without meaning.

They rented rooms in a nice house off Tottenham Court Road, where Rezia sat at the table decorating hats for their landlady, Mrs Filmer, and her friends.

"The English are so serious," she would say, putting her arms around Septimus.

At the office Mr Brewer was proud of him; Septimus had won medals.

Rezia wanted to see London. Together they went to the Tower of London and to Buckingham Palace to stand in a crowd to see the King. And there were the smart English shops – hat shops, dress shops, shops with leather bags in the window, where she would stand gazing. But what she wanted was children.

Five years of marriage passed. She must have a son like Septimus, she said. But nobody could be like Septimus: so gentle, so serious, so clever. Mrs Filmer's daughter was expecting another baby. Rezia could not grow old and have no children! She was very lonely, she was very unhappy. She cried for the first time since they were married. Far away he heard her crying. But he felt nothing.

Each time she cried in this silent, hopeless way, he felt nothing.

At last, he dropped his head on his hands, like an actor in a play, aware that it was not sincere. He gave up. Now other people must help him.

Nothing could reach him. Rezia put him to bed and sent for Mrs Filmer's family doctor. Dr Holmes examined him. There was nothing at all the matter, he said. When he felt like that himself, Dr Holmes said, he took the day off and played golf, or he went to the theatre with his wife. Oh, what a relief! What a kind man! thought Rezia.

So there was nothing the matter, except for the crime of not feeling, for which **human nature** had found him guilty and would put him to death. He had not cared when Evans was killed; that was the worst. But he had **committed** other crimes, too: he had married his wife without loving her; he had lied to her; he had offended Miss Isabel Pole. His punishment was death.

Dr Holmes came again and brushed it all aside – the headaches, sleeplessness, fears, dreams. Health is mostly in our own control, he said. Septimus must put on weight, play a sport, take up a hobby. Dr Holmes owed his own excellent health to his interest in old furniture, he said, looking in the mirror.

When the fool came again, Septimus refused to see him. Did he indeed? said Dr Holmes and he had to give the charming Mrs Smith a friendly push to get past her into her husband's bedroom.

"So you're in a bad mood," Dr Holmes said, sitting down by his patient, who had actually talked to his wife of killing himself.

Wasn't a husband responsible for protecting his wife? Wouldn't it be better to do something instead of lying in bed? For Dr Holmes had forty years' experience behind him and he could promise Mr Smith that there was nothing the matter with him. Next time he came, Dr Holmes hoped to find Smith out of bed and not worrying his charming little wife.

Human Nature, that horrible creature, was coming after him, with his blood-red nose. Dr Holmes was after him. Holmes came every day. Their only chance was to escape, without letting Holmes know. They could go to Italy, or anywhere, away from Dr Holmes.

But Rezia did not understand him. Dr Holmes was such a kind man, who only wanted to help them.

So everyone was against him. The whole world was shouting: kill yourself, kill yourself, for our sakes. But why should he kill himself for their sakes? There were still pleasures: good food, the heat of the sun. And how would one do it? With a knife? With gas? He was too weak; he could hardly lift his hand. It was at that moment (Rezia was out shopping) that Evans spoke to him.

"Evans, Evans!" he cried.

Then Rezia came in with flowers she had bought from a poor man in the street, wild with terror because Septimus was talking to himself. She sent at once for Dr Holmes, since her husband was mad and hardly knew her.

"You monster! You monster!" cried Septimus, seeing Human Nature, that is Dr Holmes, entering the room.

"Now what's all this? Talking nonsense to frighten your wife?" said Dr Holmes, kindly. He would give him something to make him sleep. And of course they may go to Harley Street, if they could afford it and if they had no confidence in him, said Dr Holmes, looking not quite so kind.

———————

It was exactly twelve o'clock by Big Ben, as Clarissa Dalloway laid her green dress on her bed, and the Warren Smiths walked down Harley Street for their appointment with Sir William Bradshaw. That must be his house, with the big grey car in front of it, thought Rezia, as the echo of Big Ben died away.

Indeed the splendid grey car was Sir William's. Matching its elegant grey paint, there were grey furs and blankets inside, which kept Lady Bradshaw warm while she waited for her husband during his visits to patients out of town. For Sir William would often travel sixty miles or more into the country to visit the unhappy rich, who could afford the very large price he rightly charged for his advice. Lady Bradshaw waited with the furs and blankets on her knees, thinking sometimes of the patient, sometimes of the growing wall of gold, which would protect her from all worries.

Sir William himself was no longer young. He had worked very hard, earned his excellent position through his own ability (being the son of a shopkeeper), and loved his profession. Its difficulties and the demands of his many patients had given him a heavy, tired look and, together with his silver-grey hair, one of great importance. His skill, his knowledge, his sympathy and his understanding of the human mind could be trusted completely.

The first moment the Warren Smiths came into the room he could see that it was an extremely serious case – a case of complete breakdown of mind and body, he judged in two or three minutes. He wrote the patient's answers to his careful questions on a pink card.

How long had Dr Holmes been seeing him?

Six weeks.

Dr Holmes had said there was nothing the matter? Ah yes, (those family doctors! thought Sir William. It took half his time to undo their mistakes and some could never be undone).

"You won medals in the War?"

The patient only repeated the word "war" and could not answer.

"Yes," Rezia told the doctor.

"And they have a good opinion of you at your office?" Sir William said. "So you are not worried about money?"

He had committed a terrible crime, he had been judged by human nature and his punishment was death.

"I have . . . I have . . ." he began, "committed a crime –"

"He has done nothing wrong at all," Rezia promised the doctor. If Mr Smith would wait, said Sir William, he would speak to Mrs Smith in the next room. Her husband was very seriously ill, Sir William said. Had he talked of killing himself?

Oh, he had, she cried, but he did not mean it. Of course not. It was only a matter of rest, said Sir William, a long rest in bed. There was a charming **nursing home** in the country where her husband would be looked after perfectly. Away from her? she asked. Unfortunately, yes, since the people we care for most are not good for us when we are ill. But he was not mad, was he? Sir William said he never spoke of "madness"; he called it "not having control". But her husband did not like doctors. He would refuse to go there. Simply and kindly Sir William explained to her the seriousness of the case. He had talked of killing himself. There was no choice. He would lie in bed in a beautiful house in the country. The nurses were admirable. Sir William would visit him once a week. Now if Mrs Warren Smith was certain she had no more questions – he never hurried his patients – they would return to her husband.

So they returned to the greatest of all men, the criminal who faced his judges, to Septimus Warren Smith, who sat staring, whispering messages about beauty.

"We have had our little talk," said Sir William.

"He says you are very, very ill," Rezia cried.

"We have been arranging that you should go into a home," said Sir William.

"One of Holmes's homes?" said Septimus, with an ugly smile.

Sir William, who attached great importance to clothing and manners, did not like the look of this untidy young man. He never had time for reading himself and disliked educated people who came into his room and suggested that doctors are not educated men.

"One of *my* homes, Mr Warren Smith," he said, "where we will teach you to rest."

And there was just one thing more. He was quite certain that when Mr Warren Smith was well he was the last person in the world who wished to frighten his wife. But he had talked of killing himself.

"We all have low moods," said Sir William.

Once you fall, Septimus repeated to himself, Human Nature is on you. Holmes and Bradshaw are on you. Would he avoid punishment if he confessed his crime?

"I – I –" Septimus started.

But what was his crime? He could not remember it.

"Yes?" Sir William encouraged him. (It was getting late.)

"I – I –" Septimus started.

"Try to think about yourself as little as possible," said Sir William, kindly. Really, the man should not be out in public. Was there anything else they wished to ask him? He would make all the arrangements (he said quietly to Rezia) and let her know between five and six that evening.

"Trust everything to me," he said, and showed them to the door.

Never in her life had Rezia felt such pain! She had asked for help and he had failed them! Sir William Bradshaw was not a nice man.

But what more did she want? Sir William gave his patients three quarters of an hour exactly, and the doctor himself must keep control, or he would fail. He must command control – so he ordered rest in bed, alone, in silence, without friends, without books – for which the friends and family of his patients were always deeply grateful.

But Rezia Warren Smith cried, walking down Harley Street at a quarter to one, that she did not like that man.

––––––––

Striking together every quarter of an hour, the clocks of Harley Street divided and controlled the June day. So time marched on until a clock in Oxford Street announced that it was half-past one. Hugh Whitbread was at Lady Bruton's front door with a bunch of red flowers in his hand, for he never failed to remember the manners of the perfect English gentleman. Lady Bruton preferred Richard Dalloway, of course, who arrived a moment later, but she would let no one criticize her poor dear Hugh. She could never forget his kindness – he had been extraordinarily kind – though exactly when that had been she could no longer remember.

There was something she needed their help with, but they would eat first, of course.

She laid Hugh's flowers down beside her plate and the food was carried silently in by white-capped servants. She must wait until the coffee was served before asking for their help, Lady Bruton reminded herself.

"Do you know who's in town?" said Lady Bruton suddenly, as Hugh helped himself to a large amount of chicken. "Our old friend Peter Walsh."

They all smiled. Peter Walsh! Richard Dalloway liked the poor man and would be very pleased to see him. And all three remembered the same thing – how Peter had been so much in love with Clarissa. But then he had been rejected, had gone to work in India and made a terrible mess of things.

Peter Walsh had been in love with Clarissa, Richard thought. Straight after lunch he would go home and tell her, in his way, that he loved her.

"Yes, Peter Walsh has come back," said Lady Bruton. He had returned, beaten, unsuccessful, to their safe shores. But it was impossible to help him; there was some fault in his character. Hugh Whitbread could certainly mention Peter's name to the heads of government offices, he could write letters, but it would not lead to anything permanent because of Peter's character.

"He's in trouble with some woman," said Lady Bruton, and of course, they had all guessed *that*. "However, we shall hear the whole story from Peter himself," she said, wanting to leave the subject now, for she had very little interest in Peter Walsh. Nothing mattered more at this moment than the project she had begun, and the letter she wished to have published about it in *The Times* newspaper. No one wrote letters to *The Times* as admirably as Hugh Whitbread, so if he wrote for her and Richard advised her, she was sure to get it right. But Hugh was very slow to finish eating, and the coffee would not be brought until he had finished. She was getting impatient.

At last Hugh was finished, the coffee was served and Lady Bruton's papers were fetched. Hugh slowly and carefully made corrections with his fine silver pen, and when he finally read out the letter Lady Bruton felt certain that it was a great success.

Lunch and letter-writing over, Lady Bruton led them to the hall, where they took their gloves from the table, and offered their thanks.

"We shall see you at our party tonight?" Richard said.

The letter-writing was done; she needed their help no more. Lady Bruton stood stiff and splendid again. She might come, or she might not, she said, standing at her door, very handsome, very upright.

Her guests left and Millicent Bruton went up to her room to lie on her sofa, to rest, not to sleep. She was not asleep, just sleepy and heavy, sleepy and heavy, as if lying in a flower-filled field in the sunshine on this hot June day, with the bees going round and round. She always went back to those fields in Devon, riding Patty her horse, with her brothers. And there were her father and mother in the garden under the trees, drinking tea, as she crawled back through the bushes after their games, so as not to be seen.

---

Touching his hat politely, Richard Dalloway parted from Hugh at the street corner. Really, an hour in the man's company was all he could bear, and he was, after all, impatient to go straight to Clarissa. But he should arrive holding something. Flowers? Yes, since he had no skill at choosing presents. Yes, an armful of flowers, to tell her he loved her. For they never spoke of that feeling and hadn't for years. The time comes when one is too shy to say it, he thought, setting off to Westminster, with his great bunch of red and white roses close to his chest. He would say it at once, holding out his flowers: "I love you." Why not? When he thought of the War and the many thousands of poor men who had died – really, it was wonderful to be walking across London to tell Clarissa that he loved her. He had once been jealous of Peter, but she had often told him she had been right not to marry him, and he believed her. Happiness is this, he thought, approaching his door. Big Ben was beginning to strike, first the warning, musical; then the hour, final.

The sound of the bells flooded Clarissa's drawing room, where she sat at her writing table, worried, annoyed. She had not invited Ellie Henderson to her party on purpose but now Mrs

Marsham had sent a message saying "Ellie so much wanted to come." But why should she invite all the dull women in London to her parties? Why should Mrs Marsham get involved? And all this time Elizabeth was shut away with Miss Kilman, praying. With great dignity and directness, Big Ben struck three, and someone was at the door. Who could it be at this hour? Good heavens, three o'clock already and what a surprise! In came Richard, holding out flowers – red and white roses. (But he could not manage to say aloud those words.)

How lovely, she said, taking his flowers. She understood; his Clarissa understood, without him speaking. And was lunch amusing, she asked. How was Lady Bruton? Must she invite Ellie Henderson to their party? Mrs Marsham had sent a message. That woman Kilman was upstairs.

"But let us sit down for five minutes," said Richard.

Peter Walsh was back. He had visited and she had been mending her dress.

"He was remembering Bourton, and I thought how I might have married him," she said, thinking of Peter playing with his knife. "He's just as he always was, you know."

They were talking about him at lunch, said Richard. (But he could not tell her that he loved her. He held her hand. Happiness is this, he thought.) Hugh was also at lunch and they had been writing a letter to *The Times* for Lady Bruton. That was all Hugh was good for. She had seen him earlier, too!

"And our dear Miss Kilman?" he asked.

"She came just after lunch and is shut away with Elizabeth," she said. "I suppose they're praying."

Good heavens! He didn't like it, but these things pass if you let them.

"She was in a raincoat and had an umbrella," said Clarissa.

He had not said "I love you", but he held her hand. Happiness is this, he thought.

And what about Ellie Henderson? Why should Mrs Marsham tell Clarissa who to invite?

"Poor Ellie," said Richard. And if Clarissa worried about these parties he would not let her give them. But he must go.

He stood for a moment as if he were about to say something; and she wondered what. There is a dignity in people, Clarissa thought, in their independence, that one must accept. It was something one should not take from one's husband, or part with oneself.

Richard went out and returned with a pillow and a blanket.

"An hour's complete rest after lunch," he said, and left.

How like him! He would go on saying "An hour's complete rest after lunch" to the end of time, because a doctor had ordered it after her influenza. And since he had brought a pillow, she would lie down . . . But why did she suddenly feel so unhappy? She searched here and there – no, it was not about Elizabeth and Miss Kilman. It was something Peter had said, and Richard had added to it. Her parties! That was it! Both of them criticized her very unfairly for her parties. Peter thought she was a snob and liked having famous people around her. Richard just thought she was silly to make herself tired when it was bad for her heart. And they were both quite wrong. What she liked was simply life.

"That's what I do it for," she said, speaking aloud, to life.

But suppose Peter said to her, "Yes, but what's the point of your parties?" All she could say was that they were an offering, as important to her as love was to him. She wanted to bring people together – to combine, to create. It was her gift. She had nothing else of the slightest importance to give.

It was enough that one day followed another, that one woke in the morning, saw the sky, walked in the park, met Hugh Whitbread. Then suddenly there was Peter; and then Richard's roses. That was enough. After that, how unbelievable death was. And no one in the whole world would know how she had loved it all; how every moment . . .

The door opened. Elizabeth came in very quietly, knowing that her mother was resting. She was dark-haired, with dark eyes in a pale, gentle face. As a child she had laughed, but now at seventeen she had become very serious, and Clarissa could not understand why.

Elizabeth stood quite still and looked at her mother. And there was Miss Kilman outside the door, in her raincoat, listening to everything they said.

Yes, Miss Kilman was in a raincoat, but she had her reasons. First, it was cheap; second, she was over forty and did not dress to please. If she had not been so poor, she would not be taking jobs from rich people like the Dalloways. To be fair, Mr Dalloway had been kind. But Mrs Dalloway had not. Miss Kilman believed she had a perfect right to anything that the Dalloways did for her.

She had been robbed of happiness. For surely a girl has a right to some kind of happiness? And she had never been happy, being so awkward, so plain and so poor. And then, just as she had a chance to do well as a teacher at Miss Dolby's school, the War came. She had never been able to tell lies. It was true that her family was originally German and their name was once spelled Kiehlman, but her brother had been killed. Miss Dolby asked her to leave because Miss Kilman would not pretend that all Germans were evil. She had German friends; the only happy days of her life had been spent in Germany! She had had to take any small job she could. Then Mr Dalloway had generously allowed her to teach his daughter history.

She stood on the soft carpet, outside the door. Instead of lying on a sofa, Mrs Dalloway should have been in a factory, or in a shop! But since God had come to Miss Kilman two years and three months ago, she pitied women like Clarissa Dalloway from the bottom of her heart. Bitter and burning, she had gone into a church two years and three months ago. She had listened to the word of God, she had heard the boys singing, tears had run down her face.

Now when the hot and painful feelings boiled within her, this hatred of Mrs Dalloway, this anger with the world, she thought of God and became calm. She looked coolly at Mrs Dalloway, who came out with her daughter.

Elizabeth said she had forgotten her gloves and ran upstairs to find them because Miss Kilman and her mother hated each other. She could not bear to see them together.

But Miss Kilman did not hate Mrs Dalloway. She felt pity. Fool! she thought. You have known neither sadness nor pleasure; you have wasted your life! A wish rose in Miss Kilman to bring her down to her knees, to ruin her!

Clarissa was shocked. How could this woman, a woman who believed in God, have taken her daughter from her! How could this ugly woman, without any kindness, know the meaning of life!

"You are taking Elizabeth shopping?" Mrs Dalloway said.

Miss Kilman said she was. They stood there. Miss Kilman was silent. She had always earned her living. Out of her small income, she gave money to the charities she supported, while this woman did nothing, believed nothing. But here was Elizabeth, a little out of breath, the beautiful girl.

So they were going shopping, Clarissa thought. It was odd how, second by second, the monster simply became Miss Kilman in a raincoat, whom Heaven knows Clarissa would have liked to help. Saying goodbye, Clarissa laughed.

They went downstairs together, Miss Kilman and Elizabeth.

Then suddenly Clarissa cried out violently from the top of the stairs, for this woman was taking her daughter from her, "Remember our party tonight!"

But Elizabeth had already opened the front door; there was a van passing and she did not answer.

Clarissa went back into the drawing room. Had she ever tried to change anyone? Didn't she simply wish everybody to be themselves? And out of the window she watched the old lady opposite climbing upstairs, as she had seen her many times before. Let her climb upstairs if she wanted to; let her stop, go into her bedroom, stand at the window and disappear back into the room. There was a dignity about it, something private and solemn to be admired – an old woman looking out of the window, quite **unaware** that she was being watched. It was a sight that made Clarissa want to cry. The mystery of life was simply this, thought Clarissa: here was one room, there was another. But the hateful Miss Kilman would destroy it, this freedom, this right to be oneself.

Big Ben struck the half-hour.

How extraordinary it was to see the old lady (they had been neighbours for so many years) move away from the window, as if she were forced to move by that solemn sound. But where to?

Then the bright little bells of the other clock sounded, the clock which always struck two minutes after Big Ben, and with them the thought of all sorts of little things came flooding in – Mrs Marsham, Ellie Henderson, glasses.

—————

At the sound of the late clock, Miss Kilman paused in the street for a moment, talking under her breath. "It is human weakness," she said.

She had expected Clarissa Dalloway to insult her, to laugh at her for being ugly and awkward. But Miss Kilman had failed, for she minded the way she looked and talked beside Clarissa. But why did she want to be like her? Mrs Dalloway was not serious or good. Her life was empty. She hated Mrs Dalloway from the bottom of her heart. Yet Doris Kilman had been defeated. She had nearly cried when Clarissa Dalloway laughed at her. But she would think about something else, until she reached the end of the street. At least she had Elizabeth.

But no one knew the pain! The world had rejected her, first for her ugly body, which people could not bear to look at. And for a woman of course, that meant never meeting the opposite sex, never coming first with anyone. Sometimes, it seemed to her that, except for Elizabeth, all she lived for was her simple comforts: her dinner, her tea, her hot water bottle at night. But one must fight, one must pray. But why should she have to suffer when women like Clarissa Dalloway escaped?

Miss Kilman was still talking to herself when Elizabeth turned into the shop. What department did she want? Elizabeth interrupted.

"**Petticoats**," Miss Kilman answered, and marched straight to the lift.

Up they went, and Elizabeth guided her to the petticoats, as if she were a big child. The shop girl thought Miss Kilman was mad.

Elizabeth began to wonder, as the girl wrapped up the petticoat, what Miss Kilman was thinking. They must now have their tea, said Miss Kilman, controlling herself.

Sitting opposite her in the tea room, Elizabeth began to wonder whether Miss Kilman was very hungry. She had a way of looking again and again at a plate of cakes on the table next to them. When a child came and took a cake, could Miss Kilman really mind it? Yes, she did mind; she had wanted that cake – the pink one. The pleasure of eating was almost the only pure pleasure left to her, but she was defeated even in that!

Often, after Elizabeth's lessons, Miss Kilman would stay and talk. She would talk about her unhappiness, about the war, about books, about meetings. Not everyone thought the English were right about everything, she said. There were other points of view.

Would Elizabeth like to come with her and listen to Mr Somebody (a most extraordinary-looking old man)? All professions – law, medicine, politics – are open to young women now, Miss Kilman said. Was it her fault that her own chance to have a profession had been ruined? Good heavens, no, said Elizabeth.

Her mother was always very, very nice to Miss Kilman, and gave her flowers when they were sent some from Bourton, but Miss Kilman and her mother were terrible together. They had nothing to say to each other and what interested Miss Kilman bored her mother. But then Miss Kilman was awfully clever. Elizabeth had never thought about the poor. The Dalloways lived with everything they wanted. Lucy took her mother breakfast in bed every day. But Miss Kilman said one day, "My grandfather had a little shop." She made one feel so small, so inferior.

Miss Kilman took another cup of tea. Elizabeth sat perfectly upright; no, she did not want anything else. She looked for her gloves. Oh, but she must not go! Miss Kilman could not let her go – this beautiful young girl, whom she loved! Her large hand opened and shut on the table.

Miss Kilman said, "I've not quite finished yet."

Of course, then, Elizabeth would wait. But it was rather hot.

"Are you going to the party tonight?" Miss Kilman said. Elizabeth supposed she was; her mother wanted her to go.

Elizabeth must not attach too much importance to parties, Miss Kilman said, holding the last piece of her cake between her thick fingers.

She did not much like parties, Elizabeth said. Miss Kilman

opened her mouth, pushing her chin forward, and swallowed down the last two inches of cake. She cleaned her fingers and washed the tea round in her cup.

She was about to crack open, she felt. The pain was unbearable. All she wanted was to make Elizabeth hers forever and then die. But to sit here, unable to think of anything to say, was too much. To see Elizabeth turning against her, finding her ugly, was too much to bear.

"I never go to parties," said Miss Kilman, just to prevent Elizabeth leaving. "People don't ask me to parties." She knew she should not show such self-pity, but she could not help it. She had suffered so horribly. "Why should they ask me?" she said. "I'm plain, I'm unhappy." She knew it was foolish. But it was all those people walking past with their shopping who hated her that made her say it. However, she was Doris Kilman. She had been to university. She had made her own way in the world.

"I don't **pity** myself," she said. "I pity . . ." She meant to say "your mother" but she could not, not to Elizabeth. "I pity other people more," she said.

Like a gentle horse who has been led quietly to the gate of a field without knowing why, and stands there wanting only to run away, Elizabeth sat silent. Was Miss Kilman going to say anything more?

"Don't forget me," said Doris Kilman, her voice trembling. The horse raced right away to the end of the field in terror.

Elizabeth turned her head. The waitress came. One had to pay at the desk, Elizabeth said, getting up. And Miss Kilman felt the insides of her body being dragged out of her, stretching as Elizabeth crossed the room. And then, with a final pull, nodding her head very politely, Elizabeth went.

She had gone. Miss Kilman sat in the tea room among the cakes, struck by shocks of suffering. Elizabeth had gone. Mrs Dalloway had won. Beauty and **youth** had gone.

Then she got up heavily, walking uncertainly among the little tables, until someone came after her with her petticoat. She lost her way among the leather bags, baby clothes, medicines, flowers, and at last came out on to the street.

She would find a church. She would hide her face in her hands and pray, trying to free herself both of hatred and love. But the path to God was not smooth.

Elizabeth waited in Victoria Street for a bus. It was so nice to be out in the fresh air and perhaps she need not go home just yet. She would get on to a bus. And already, as she stood there in her fine clothes, it was beginning . . . People were beginning to compare her to a tall tree, a pale rose, a shy young deer, and she wanted to escape it. She so much preferred being left alone in the country with her father and the dogs, away from London, away from parties, away from men falling in love with her.

Buses came and went, but which should she get on? She held herself back, not wanting to push, very straight, very calm, almost beautiful. Suddenly Elizabeth stepped forward and confidently got on a bus, in front of everybody. She took a seat outside, on the top. She was an adventurer, delighted to be free. The fresh air was lovely. It was like riding a horse, to be rushing up Whitehall, with the wind in her hair.

It was always talking about her own sufferings that made Miss Kilman so difficult. But was she right? Wasn't giving up hours and hours every day for government meetings (she hardly ever saw her father in London) helping the poor?

She liked people who were ill. All professions are open to young women now, Miss Kilman had said. So she might be a doctor. She might be a farmer. Animals are often ill. She might own a lot of land and have people working for her. She would visit them in their cottages. The bus stopped by Somerset House, so splendid, so serious. She liked the feeling of people busily working inside, in all of its offices. She might be a very good farmer, she thought, looking at Somerset House. It made her quite determined, despite what her mother might say, to become either a farmer or a doctor.

But it was better to say nothing about it. It seemed so silly. It was the sort of thing that did sometimes happen, when one was alone. The sight of a splendid, serious building had more power than any book Miss Kilman lent her to make her thoughts break to the surface, just for a moment.

And now she must go home. She must dress for dinner. But what was the time? Where was a clock?

A breath of wind blew a cloud over the sun and the bright colour of the buses suddenly faded. The clouds gathered and moved, now giving light to the earth, now darkness.

———

The coming and going of shadow and light, which made the walls grey one moment, and the bananas bright yellow the next, seemed like a sign to Septimus Warren Smith, lying on the sofa in his sitting room. The sound of water was in the room and the voices of birds singing came through the waves. Far away he heard dogs barking. *Fear no more*, says the heart in the body.

He was not afraid. Nature was showing him signs on the wall.

Rezia, sitting at the table with a hat in her hands, watched him, and saw him smiling. He was happy then. But she could not bear to see him smiling. One's husband should not look strange like that – always staring, laughing, sitting silent for hour after hour, or taking her arm and telling her to write. The drawer was full of those writings: about war, about Shakespeare, about how there is no death. Sometimes he waved his hands and cried out that he knew the truth! He knew everything! His friend who was killed, Evans, had come, he said. He was singing behind the wall. She wrote it down exactly as he said. Some things were very beautiful, others were complete nonsense. And he always stopped in the middle, changed his mind, wanted to add something, hearing something new.

But she heard nothing.

And once they found the girl who cleaned the room reading one of those papers and laughing. It was terrible, for it made Septimus cry out about how people tear each other to pieces. "Holmes is after us," he would say. And he would invent stories about Holmes, shouting with laughter or anger, for Dr Holmes seemed to him to stand for something horrible. He called Dr Holmes "Human Nature". Then there were his dreams. He had drowned in the sea, he used to say, with the birds screaming over him. He would look over the edge of the sofa, down into the sea. Or he would hear music and cry, when really it was only some man shouting in the street. That was the worst thing of all, to see a brave man like Septimus, who had fought in the War, with tears running down his cheeks. Sometimes he would suddenly cry that he was falling down, down into the flames! She would actually look for flames, it was so real. But there was nothing. They were alone in the room. It was a dream, she would tell him, but sometimes she was frightened, too.

Through his half-closed eyes he could see the shape of her: her little black body at the table, her face and her hands, turning the hat, picking something up, looking for something. She was making a hat for Mrs Filmer's married daughter – he had forgotten her name.

"What is the name of Mrs Filmer's married daughter?" he asked.

"Mrs Peters," said Rezia. She was worried the hat was too small, she said, holding it up for him to see.

He covered his eyes so that he might see only a little of her face at a time, first the chin, then the nose, then the forehead, in case it had some terrible mark on it. But no, there she was, perfectly natural, sewing, her lips tight together. There was nothing terrible about it, he thought, checking again for a second and a third time.

"It's too small for Mrs Peters," said Septimus.

For the first time for days he was speaking as he used to! Of course, it was much too small, she said. But Mrs Peters had chosen it.

He took the hat out of her hands and laughed at it. How happy she was about that! They hadn't laughed together like this for weeks.

"There," she said, putting a rose on one side of the hat. Never in her life had she felt so happy!

But that looked even more silly, Septimus said. Now the poor woman would look like a pig at a country fête. (Nobody ever made her laugh like Septimus did.)

He would help her, for he had a wonderful eye. He began to put odd colours together.

"She shall have a beautiful hat!" he said, picking up this and that, while Rezia knelt by his side, looking over his shoulder.

Now it was finished and she must sew it together. But she must be very careful to keep it exactly as he had made it.

So she sewed, her strong little fingers flying. The sun might come and go on the walls, but he would wait in this warm place.

"There it is," said Rezia, holding up Mrs Peters' hat.

It was wonderful. He had never done anything which made him feel so proud. Mrs Peters' hat was so real, so solid.

It would always make her happy to see that hat. He had become himself then. He had laughed. They had been alone together.

Then there was a knock at the door. Could it be Sir William Bradshaw already?

No! It was only the little girl with the evening paper. Rezia got down on her knees beside Mrs Filmer's grandchild, as she did every evening, with a bag of toffees, laughing and kissing her.

They danced round the room, laughing. Septimus was very tired. He was very happy. He would sleep. He shut his eyes. But as soon as he saw nothing, the sounds of the game became stranger, like the cries of people searching and not finding. They had lost him!

He jumped up in terror. There was nobody there (Rezia had taken the little girl home to her mother). He was alone. That was his punishment: to be alone for ever. Where were the voices of the dead? Where he had once seen mountains, faces, beauty, there was a wall.

"Evans!" he cried. There was no answer.

Rezia came into the room, talking. She sat on the end of the sofa.

They were perfectly happy now, she said. For she could say anything to him now. That was almost the first thing she had felt about him when he came shyly into the café that night in Milan, with his English friends. She knew he was English, with his beautiful fresh colour, his big nose, his bright eyes, his way of sitting a little bent over. She had never seen him wild or drunk, only suffering sometimes because of the terrible war. But he would put it all aside when she came in. She could say anything to him and he understood her at once. He was older than she was and so clever and serious – he could help her. And she could help him.

But now this hat. And then Sir William Bradshaw, between five and six (it was getting late).

He watched her as she sat there; he could feel her mind, like a bird, flying from branch to branch. But he remembered Bradshaw saying, "The people we care for most are not good for us when we are ill." Bradshaw had said they must be separated.

"What right has Bradshaw to say 'must' to me?" he demanded.

"It is because you talked of killing yourself," said Rezia. (Thankfully, she could say anything to Septimus now.)

So he was in their power! Holmes and Bradshaw were after him! She should get out his papers, the things he had written, the things she had written for him. She emptied them on to the sofa: drawings with circles, stars, faces, waves; and his writings – how the dead sing behind bushes, his conversations with Shakespeare, Evans' messages from the dead, the meaning of the world. "Burn them!" he cried.

But some were very beautiful, Rezia thought. She would tie them up.

Even if they took him, she said, she would go with him. Nobody could separate them, she said.

Sitting beside him, she tied up the parcel of papers. She was a flowering tree, he thought. Gazing from its branches was the face of someone who had reached a safe place, fearing no one. She did not fear Holmes and Bradshaw, the judges who saw nothing clearly but still made the rules. She had defeated them.

"There!" she said. The papers were tied up. She would put them away.

And, sitting beside him again, she said nothing could separate them.

Then she got up to go into the bedroom to pack their things. But she heard voices downstairs and ran down to prevent Dr Holmes coming up.

Septimus could hear her talking to Holmes on the stairs.

"My dear lady, I have come as a friend," Holmes was saying.

"No. I will not allow you to see my husband," she said.

He could see her, like a little bird, with her wings spread, standing in his way. But Holmes did not give up.

"My dear lady, allow me . . ." Holmes said, putting her aside. (Holmes was a powerful man.)

Holmes was coming upstairs. Holmes would throw open the door. Holmes would get him. But no; Holmes would not get him, nor Bradshaw. Getting up from the sofa, walking uncertainly, he considered Mrs Filmer's nice clean bread knife. Ah, but one mustn't spoil that. The gas fire? But it was too late now. Holmes was coming. There remained only the window − the awkward and rather theatrical business of opening the window and throwing himself out. It was Holmes and Bradshaw's idea of tragedy, not his or Rezia's (for she understood him). Holmes and Bradshaw liked that sort of thing. (He sat on the edge of the window.) But he would wait till the very last moment. He did not want to die. Life was good. The sun was hot. But human beings − what did they want? An old man came down the stairs in the house opposite and stared at him. Holmes was at the door.

"I'll give it to you!" Septimus cried and threw himself violently down.

"The coward!" cried Dr Holmes, rushing through the door.

Rezia ran to the window. She saw; she understood. Mrs Filmer made her hide her eyes in the bedroom. People ran up and down the stairs. Dr Holmes came in, as white as a sheet and shaking all over, with a glass in his hand. She must be brave and drink what was in it. Who could have imagined it? It was a sudden decision. No one was at all to blame, he told Mrs Filmer. And why he did it, Dr Holmes could not understand.

Rezia drank the sweet stuff in the glass and it seemed to her that she was opening long windows, and stepping out into a garden. But where? The clock was striking – one, two, three . . . How sensible the sound was compared to all the knocking and whispering. She was falling asleep. But the clock went on striking, four, five, six . . . She put on her hat and ran through the fields, somewhere near the sea. They sat looking out at the sea.

"He is dead," she said, smiling at the poor old woman who guarded her. They wouldn't bring him in here, would they? Oh no, oh no, said Mrs Filmer. But they were carrying him away now and shouldn't she be told? Married people ought to be together, Mrs Filmer thought. But they must do as the doctor said.

"Let her sleep," said Dr Holmes, and she saw the large shape of his body, dark against the window.

---

The light, high bell of an ambulance sounded. It is one of the great achievements of society, Peter Walsh thought. That was progress. Quickly, cleanly, the ambulance rushed to the hospital, having picked up some poor creature – someone knocked down at a crossing perhaps, as might so easily happen to oneself. Every vehicle pulled aside to let the ambulance pass, and busy men pictured someone's poor wife inside. But one must stop these thoughts of doctors and dead bodies before they went too far, and made one sentimental. I would stand here and cry, he thought, if no one could see – for one may do as one chooses in private. For moments like these, in which things came together, like life and death, took one's breath away.

Years ago Clarissa had told him, sitting together on the top of a bus, that she felt herself everywhere – in everything there was. It helped her to believe, for she had a horror of death, that the unseen part of us might survive in people or even places after death, perhaps.

Looking back over their long friendship of more than thirty years, he understood something of what she meant. However short, broken and painful their meetings were (this morning, for example, they were interrupted by Elizabeth coming in like a beautiful, long-legged horse) the effect of them on his life was enormous. She had affected him more than any person he had ever known, and she appeared to him like this, in all her moods, without him wishing it. One scene after another at Bourton came back to him . . .

He had reached his hotel. He crossed the hall, collected his key and some letters and went upstairs. He pictured her most often at Bourton, in the late summer, on top of a hill – her cloak blowing, her hands on her hair – crying out to them that she could see the river below. Then after dinner, old Joseph Breitkopf would sit at the piano and sing in a trembling voice, and they would try not to laugh. But they could not help it – they were always laughing, laughing at nothing.

Oh, this blue envelope was a letter from her! That was her writing. Reading her letter required a huge effort; it would be another of their painful meetings. "How heavenly it was to see him. She must tell him that." That was all.

But it upset and annoyed him. He wished she hadn't written it. Why couldn't she leave him alone? After all, she had married

Dalloway and lived with him in perfect happiness all these years.

"Heavenly to see you. She must say so!" He folded the note and put it away. Nothing would make him read it again!

To get that letter to him by six o'clock she must have written it as soon as he left her. It was very like her. She was upset by his visit. She had remembered perhaps something he had said – how they would change the world if she married him. But now, instead, there was being middle aged and ordinary. And then, with her energy for life, her toughness, her power to overcome difficulties, which was greater than anyone's he had ever known, she forced herself to put all that aside. He could see her going to her writing table, tears running down her cheeks, wanting to make him happy, and writing that one line . . . "Heavenly to see you!" And she meant it.

But it would not have been a success, their marriage.

He pulled off his boots and emptied his pockets. Out came his knife and a photo of Daisy, all in white, looking charming. And he could hear the pretty, dark-haired girl crying that of course she would give him everything he wanted! And she was only twenty-four, with two children.

Indeed, what a mess he had got himself into at his age! The thought would disturb him in the night quite forcefully. Suppose they did marry? It would be fine for him, but what about her? Mrs Burgess, a sensible woman whom he trusted, had said Daisy had to think of her position in society. His absence in England might give Daisy a chance to think again. She would have to give up her children when she got divorced, and after

Peter died she would be alone, with no good friends. But Peter Walsh didn't mean to die yet! Anyway, Daisy must decide for herself, he thought, and took out his white shirt, for he might go to Clarissa's party, or to the theatre. Or he might stay in and read a book written by a man he used to know at Oxford. If he stopped working, that's what he would do – write books.

And it might be better, as Mrs Burgess said, if Daisy forgot him, or just remembered him as he was in August 1922, standing at the crossroads in the evening . . .

Yes, he would go to Clarissa's party. He would go because he wanted to ask Richard what the government thought it was doing in India. He wanted to find out what was on at the theatre, what concerts there were . . . Simply, he wanted people, conversation. He would have dinner, he would smoke a cigarette and he would walk through the warm summer night, among the lively, beautiful young people, to Westminster, to Clarissa's door.

———

The sound of voices from the dining room below brought Lucy running out of the drawing room. She had only wanted a quick look – to put a candlestick straight, to smooth her hand over a chair. And then to pause for a moment and feel how beautifully cared for everything would appear to everyone who came in. But people were already coming upstairs after dinner! She must fly down to the kitchen!

The Prime Minister was coming, Agnes said, returning to the kitchen with a tray of glasses. She had heard them saying so in the dining room when she was serving. But did Mrs

Walker, the cook, care at all if a Prime Minister was coming, with her kitchen upside down like this? Did one person more or less right now make any difference to Mrs Walker, among all the plates, pans, lemons, bread, soup bowls and pudding bowls, which seemed to be all on top of her, and so much still to be done?

They were going up to the drawing room already, said Lucy, and Mrs Dalloway had sent a message down to the kitchen: "My love to Mrs Walker." And how lovely Miss Elizabeth looked in her pink dress, Lucy said.

And there was the front-door bell already! Now the guests would come faster and faster. The hall would soon be full of gentlemen waiting while the ladies went to the room along the corridor to take off their cloaks. And old Mrs Barnet, who had been with the family for forty years, would be waiting there to help them. She came every summer, remembered mothers when they were girls, and in spite of their fine cloaks, knew perfectly well which were nice ladies and which were not.

Mrs Barnet, Clarissa's old nanny, is such a dear old thing, said Lady Lovejoy to her daughter, as they climbed the stairs. Then standing stiff and tall beside Mr Wilkins (who was hired for parties), at the top of the stairs, she said to him, "Lady and Miss Lovejoy."

"Lady and Miss Lovejoy," announced Wilkins, who bowed and stood straight admirably between each announcement. "Sir John and Lady Needham . . . Miss Weld . . . Mr Peter Walsh."

"How delightful to see you!" said Clarissa to Peter. She said it to everyone. How delightful to see you! She was at her worst – insincere, shallow. It was a great mistake to have come, for he knew no one.

Oh, it was going to be a complete failure, Clarissa was certain, as dear old Lord Lexham stood explaining that his wife had caught a cold at the Buckingham Palace garden party. She could see Peter in the corner, criticizing her. And why did she do these things, after all? Why did she try to rise to such heights and stand in the fire? But it was better to burn than to fade away like Ellie Henderson! It was extraordinary how Peter put her into these states just by standing in the corner. He made her see herself, but in this extravagant way. It was foolish. But why did he come, simply to criticize? Why always take, never give? He was wandering off now, and she must speak to him. But she would not get the chance. Lord Lexham was saying that his wife would not wear her coat at the garden party because "my dear, you ladies are all alike". Yet Lady Lexham was seventy-five at least! The dear old couple! She did like Lord Lexham. And her party did matter. It made her feel quite sick to know that it was all falling flat. Anything, any explosion, any horror, was better than people wandering about, standing in the corner, not even caring to hold themselves upright, like Ellie Henderson.

Gently, by the open window, the yellow curtain with its pattern of birds blew out, and it seemed as if the birds flew right into the room. Should the windows be open, Ellie Henderson wondered. It would not matter if she started sneezing tomorrow; it was the girls with their naked shoulders she worried about. She never gave a thought to her clothes and had only thrown a large scarf over her old black dress, since her invitation to

Clarissa's party had come at the last moment. She had a feeling that Clarissa had not meant to ask her this year, and why should she, except that they had grown up together? A party was a special occasion for her, just seeing the lovely clothes. Wasn't that Elizabeth in the pink dress, looking so grown up and very, very handsome? But girls no longer seemed to wear white for their first parties, as they had when she and Clarissa were young.

So, Ellie Henderson watched, not minding that she had no one to talk to, for they were all such interesting people – politicians, she supposed, Richard Dalloway's friends. It was Richard who felt that he could not let the poor creature stand there all evening by herself.

"Well, Ellie, and how's the world treating *you*?" he said, in his kindly way. And Ellie felt that it was extraordinarily nice of him to come and talk to her.

The curtain with its birds flew out again. And Clarissa saw Ralph Lyon beat it back and go on talking. It was not a failure after all! It was going to be all right. Her party had begun. But she must stay at the top of the stairs for the present. People seemed to come all at once.

Mr and Mrs Garrod . . . Mr Hugh Whitbread . . . Lady Mary Maddox . . . announced Wilkins. She had six or seven words with each, and they went on into the rooms, into something now, not nothing, since Ralph Lyon had beaten back the curtain.

But it was too much effort. She was not enjoying it. Anybody could stand there and do this. And yet, rooted like a tree at the top of her stairs, she couldn't help feeling proud for making this happen.

They kept coming up the stairs, one after another. Mrs Mount and Celia, Herbert Ainsty, oh and Lady Bruton!

"How awfully good of you to come!" she said, and she meant it. How odd it was, watching them going into the rooms, some quite old, some –

Lady Rosseter, announced Wilkins.

Who? Who was Lady Rosseter?

"Clarissa!" She knew that voice! It was Sally Seton, after all these years! But she hadn't looked like that when Clarissa had come down the stairs at Bourton in a white dress to meet Sally Seton!

Embarrassed, laughing, they kissed each other, first one cheek, then the other. She was passing through London, could not miss the chance of meeting again! "So I pushed myself in, without an invitation . . ."

The spark had gone out of her, yet it was extraordinary to see her again, older, happier, less lovely. Clarissa took Sally's hand, turned, saw her rooms full, heard the laughter, saw the curtains blowing, and Richard's roses.

"I have five enormous boys," said Sally, still with her simple wish to be thought of first, and Clarissa loved her for still being like that.

But Wilkins was commanding her to be serious with one name.

The Prime Minister? Was it really? Ellie Henderson wondered. What a thing!

He looked so ordinary, as if he might sell biscuits in a shop, but all dressed up in gold **lace**. And to be fair, when he went around, he did it very well. He tried to look important. It was amusing to watch. Nobody looked at him; they just went on talking. Yet it was perfectly clear how he mattered to them, standing for English society in the way that he did. Old Lady Bruton advanced, looking fine in her lace, and took him into a little room, which was whispered about and guarded at once. The Prime Minister!

What snobs the English are! thought Peter Walsh. How they admire gold lace! And there was Hugh Whitbread, guarding the closed door, looking rather fatter and greyer. Peter had read his admirable letters in *The Times*, thousands of miles away in India, thankful that he was away from it all. Look at the man now, dancing forward, bending and bowing, as the Prime Minister and Lady Bruton came out. The admirable Hugh was making certain the world saw that he had something private to say to Lady Bruton as she passed. She nodded her fine old head, probably thanking him for some little thing he had done for her.

And there was Clarissa now, taking her Prime Minister through the drawing room, effortlessly, as if floating on water, in her silver-green dress. But age had brushed her and her woodenness was warmed through. She had a great dignity about her, saying goodbye to the Prime Minister as if she wished the whole world well and must now leave. So she made Peter think. (But he was not in love.)

Indeed, Clarissa felt, the Prime Minister had been good to come. Walking round the room with him she had felt the happiness of the moment, and then the emptiness. And suddenly, seeing the Prime Minister go down the stairs, she remembered her enemy, Kilman. That was real. Ah, how she hated her, and her power over Elizabeth!

Now Sir William and Lady Bradshaw were coming up the stairs. But they must find her if they wanted her. She was for the party!

"Dear Sir Harry!" she said, going up to her old friend, who was with Willie Titcomb and Herbert Ainsty, all of them laughing. Old Mrs Hilbery touched her arm. Clarissa looked so like her mother tonight, as she had first seen her walking in a garden in a grey hat. And Clarissa's eyes filled with tears, thinking of her mother walking in a garden!

But Professor Brierly and little John Hutton were not getting on and she must interrupt their quarrel. How she wished she could steal John away and sit him down at the piano in the back room, for he played so beautifully. "But there is too much noise!" she said.

And there was old Aunt Helena, in her white shawl, past eighty now, sitting in an armchair that Richard had found for her. But where was Peter? He and Aunt Helena had been such good friends. He could talk to her about India, for she had walked in its mountains, painting the flowers, sixty years ago. Ah, here he was!

"Come and talk to Aunt Helena about India," said Clarissa.

But he had not spoken to her all evening!

"We will talk later," said Clarissa, leading him up to old Miss Parry in her armchair.

"You remember Peter Walsh," said Clarissa.

Old Helena Parry did not at first, but then it came back to her.

He had been at Bourton (and Peter Walsh remembered leaving her in the drawing room that night when Clarissa had asked him to come boating).

But here came Lady Bruton. "Richard was the greatest possible help with a letter," Lady Bruton said to Clarissa. "And there's Peter Walsh!" she said (for Lady Bruton could never think of anything to say to Richard's wife, though she liked her. Really, it might have been better if Richard had married someone who could have helped him more in his work.) She shook hands with that charming failure, Peter Walsh, who should have made a name for himself but hadn't (always in difficulties with women). And, of course, wonderful old Miss Parry!

But was that Peter Walsh, his hair now grey? Lady Rosseter (who had been Sally Seton) asked herself. That was certainly old Miss Parry, who used to be so cross when Sally had stayed at Bourton. She would never forget running along the corridor naked, and being sent for by Miss Parry! And there was Clarissa! Sally caught her by the arm.

"I can't stay," Clarissa said. "Wait," she said, looking at her old friends, Peter and Sally. They must wait, she meant, until all these people had gone. "I shall come back," she said.

But Sally's voice had lost its old wonderful richness; her eyes were not as bright as they used to be when she had run down the corridor with no clothes on. She had stolen a chicken from the kitchen because she was hungry in the night; she had left an expensive book in the boat. But everybody loved her (except perhaps Papa). Her love of being the centre of everything and creating scenes would end in some awful tragedy, Clarissa used to think. Instead of which she had married a man who owned factories in Manchester. And she had five boys!

Sally and Peter were shaking hands, and Sally was laughing, remembering the past, no doubt. It was with the two of them, even more than with Richard, that Clarissa shared her past. But she must leave them because there were the Bradshaws, whom she disliked. She must go up to Lady Bradshaw (dressed in grey and silver) and say . . .

But Lady Bradshaw spoke first.

"We are shockingly late, dear Mrs Dalloway. We were embarrassed to come in," she said.

And Sir William, who looked very important, with his silver-grey hair and blue eyes, was talking privately to Richard, about politics probably. But why did the sight of him disturb her? He looked what he was – a great doctor, a man at the top of his profession, very powerful, rather tired. For think of the terrible decisions he had to make and what he had to see – people in the deepest unhappiness. Yet the sight of him made her feel that one wouldn't like Sir William to see one unhappy.

"How is your son at Eton?" she asked Lady Bradshaw.

He had just missed getting into the cricket team, because he had been sick. But his father minded even more than he did, Lady Bradshaw thought, "being nothing but a great boy himself."

Clarissa looked at Sir William, talking to Richard. He did not look in the least like a boy. She did not know what it was about him that she disliked, and Richard agreed with her. But Sir William was extraordinarily knowledgeable. He was speaking quietly to Richard about something. The effects of the War on the mind . . . The government must discuss it . . .

Wishing to share with Mrs Dalloway a sisterly pleasure in their husbands' great skill, Lady Bradshaw lowered her voice. "Just as we were leaving, my husband received a telephone call, a very sad case. A young man (that is what Sir William is telling Mr Dalloway) had killed himself. He had been in the army."

Oh! thought Clarissa, in the middle of my party, here's death.

She went on, into the little room where the Prime Minister had gone with Lady Bruton. Perhaps there was somebody there. But there was nobody. The splendid beauty of the party fell to the floor; how strange it was to come in alone in her evening dress.

Why did the Bradshaws talk of death at her party? A young man had killed himself. And they talked of it at her party. He had killed himself – but how? Her body always felt it first, when she was told suddenly of an accident. Her body burned. He had thrown himself from a window. The ground had rushed up through him, breaking him. There he lay with a thud, thud, thud in his brain, before drowning in blackness. That's how she saw it. But why had he done it?

He had thrown his life away. They went on living (she would have to go back to the party; the rooms were still crowded; people kept coming). They (all day she had been thinking of Peter, of Sally), they would grow old. He had held on to something that mattered, which in her own life lay hidden in dishonesty and lies. Death was not giving in. Death was an attempt to connect when knowing another was impossible. One was alone. But not in death.

But this young man who had killed himself – had he plunged holding on to what mattered?

Or had he gone to Sir William Bradshaw, that great doctor, yet to her mysteriously evil, and felt Sir William's power over him? Perhaps that would make him feel (indeed she felt it now), that life is unbearable.

Then (she had felt it only this morning) there was the fear of life, this terror of living life to the end. Quite often, if Richard had not been near her, reading *The Times*, she might not have survived. But because he was close, she could hide like a bird with its head on its wing and gradually recover that love of life. But that young man had killed himself.

It was her punishment to have escaped. She was forced to stand in her evening dress and to see a man disappear here, a woman there, falling down into the darkness. She was never wholly admirable. She had wanted success. And once she had been young and walked in the gardens at Bourton.

It was due to Richard that she had never been so happy. Nothing could be slow enough; nothing could last too long. No pleasure could be as great as having finished with the joys of youth.

She walked to the window. Many times, at Bourton when they were all talking, or in London when she could not sleep, she had gone to look at the sky. However foolish the idea was, she felt the country sky at Bourton, this sky above Westminster, held something of her own in it.

She opened the curtains. She looked. Oh, but how surprising! In the room opposite the old lady stared straight at her! She was going to bed. It was fascinating to watch her moving about, crossing the room, coming to stand at her window. Could the old lady see her? It was fascinating, when people were still laughing and shouting in her drawing room, to watch that old woman, quite quietly, going to bed alone. Now the old lady pulled down her blind. The clock began striking. The young man had killed himself, but she did not pity him, with all this going on. There! The old lady had put out her light. The whole house was dark now with all this going on, Clarissa repeated. And the words came back to her, "*Fear no more the heat of the sun*".

She must go back to them. But what an extraordinary night! She felt in a way very like him – the young man who had killed himself. She felt glad that he had done it; had thrown his life away while they went on living. The clock was striking. The echoes faded in the air. But she must go back. She must find Sally and Peter.

———

"But where is Clarissa?" said Peter. He was sitting on the sofa with Sally. "Where has she gone?"

Sally supposed, and Peter agreed, that there were important people there, politicians, whom Clarissa had to be nice to. She was with them. Though as a politician Richard had not been a great success? Sally supposed. And she had done things, too!

"I have five sons!" she told Peter.

Good heavens, how Sally had changed! Last time they met, Peter remembered, had been among the cauliflowers and rose bushes in the moonlight. She had marched him up and down that awful night, after the scene by the fountain, before he had caught the midnight train. Heavens, how he had cried!

That was his old trick, always playing with a pocket-knife when he got excited, thought Sally. They had been very close, she and Peter Walsh, when he was in love with Clarissa. After that awful scene over Richard, Peter had gone off to India and had had an unhappy marriage, she had heard. Now he had changed, but she still cared for him, for he was connected to her youth. She still had a little book of poetry he had given her. In those days he had wanted to write books.

"Have you written?" she asked him.

"Not a word!" said Peter Walsh, and she laughed.

He still felt the force of her character, the old Sally Seton. But who was this Rosseter, her husband?

He owned factories in Manchester. They had a huge house and armies of servants, she said with a laugh. Sally was proud of her husband. He had worked hard and earned every penny they had. "You must meet him. You would like him," she said.

And Sally used to be so poor, when she had come to Bourton. Going to Bourton had meant so much to her, she remembered, when she had been so unhappy at home. But that was all in the past now, she said. And Clarissa's marriage had been a success? Sally supposed. And that very handsome young woman, over there, by the curtains, was Elizabeth?

She was not a bit like Clarissa, Peter said.

"Oh, Clarissa!" said Sally.

She felt simply that she owed Clarissa an enormous amount. They had been true friends, and she could still see Clarissa all in white, going about the house at Bourton with her hands full of flowers. But really, how could Clarissa have married

Richard Dalloway, a man of the country, who cared only for dogs and horses? And then all this? She waved her hand at the room.

Hugh Whitbread wandered past without seeing them. "He's not going to recognize us," said Sally. "And what does the admirable Hugh do now?" she asked Peter.

He cleaned the King's boots or counted bottles at the palace, Peter told her, and she laughed. Peter's tongue was as sharp as ever!

The problem between her and Clarissa, Sally said, was that Clarissa was really a snob. She thought Sally had married beneath her, her husband being the son of a working man.

(And so Sally would go on, Peter felt, hour after hour, about the working man's son, about how people thought she had married beneath her, about her five sons. Clarissa had escaped all that.)

Was she a snob? Yes, in many ways she was. Where was she, all this time? It was getting late.

Yet how generous Clarissa was to her friends, said Sally, with a rush of emotion, which Peter used to love her for, but feared a little now. Clarissa was pure-hearted. Peter would think Sally sentimental for saying it, but she now believed that the only thing worth saying was simply what one felt. Cleverness was silly.

"But I do not know," said Peter Walsh, "what I feel."

Poor Peter, thought Sally. Why didn't Clarissa come and talk to them? That was what he wanted. All the time he was thinking only of Clarissa and playing with his knife.

He had not found life simple, Peter said. His feelings for

Clarissa had not been simple and had spoilt his life. One could not be in love twice, he said.

And Clarissa had cared for him more than she ever cared for Richard, Sally was sure of that.

"No, no, no!" said Peter. (Sally should not have said that.) Richard was a good man and of them all seemed to him the best.

And were Clarissa and Richard happy together? Sally asked. For she admitted she knew nothing about them, only imagined things, as one does. Since what can one know even of the people one lives with every day? she asked. But Peter did not agree that we know nothing. We know everything, he said; at least he did.

But this couple coming now, Sally whispered, this silver-haired man and his rather ordinary-looking wife, who had been talking to Richard – what could one know about people like that?

"That they are shallow fools who cannot be trusted," said Peter, looking at them casually. He made Sally laugh.

Sir William Bradshaw stopped at the door to look at a painting. He looked in the corner for the painter's name. His wife looked, too. Sir William Bradshaw was so interested in art.

When one was young, said Peter, one was too impatient to know people. Now that one was old, fifty-three to be exact, one could watch, one could understand, and one did not lose the power of feeling. It was true, said Sally. She felt more deeply every year.

Elizabeth there, Peter said, does not feel half of what we feel, not yet. But, said Sally, watching Elizabeth go to her father, one can see how much they love each other.

For her father had been looking at her, as he stood talking to the Bradshaws, and he had thought to himself, Who is that lovely girl? And suddenly he realized that it was his Elizabeth, and he had not recognized her, she looked so lovely in her pink dress! Elizabeth had gone to him and they stood together, glad that the party was almost over. They watched the people going, and the rooms getting emptier and emptier. And he had not meant to tell her, but he could not help it because he was proud of his daughter. He told her that he had looked at her and wondered, Who is that lovely girl? And it was his daughter! That did make her happy.

"Richard has improved. You are right," said Sally. "I shall go and talk to him. I shall say goodnight. What does the brain matter," said Lady Rosseter, getting up, "compared with the heart?"

"I will come," said Peter, but he sat on for a moment. What is this terror? What is this joy? he thought to himself. What is it that fills me with extraordinary excitement?

It is Clarissa, he said.

For there she was.

# During-reading questions

1  In the first three paragraphs of the story, what is Mrs Dalloway actually doing at the present moment? Why does this make her think of the past?

2  Who is Lucy, do you think?

3  Read up to ". . . life, London, this moment of June" on page 12 again. What do we learn about Clarissa Dalloway and Peter Walsh?

4  What is important about the telegram that Lady Bexborough receives? Why is the War not over for her, do you think?

5  What do we learn about Hugh Whitbread and his wife? How does Clarissa feel about them? What does the word "admirable" tell us about Hugh and about Clarissa?

6  When Clarissa meets Hugh, what does she remember about Peter Walsh? What do we learn about Clarissa and Peter's relationship now and in the past?

7  What do you think Clarissa means when she says that "she would not say of anyone in the world now that they were this or were that"?

8  What are Clarissa's thoughts about death? Why are the words from Shakespeare (from the play *Cymbeline*) important? Why does Clarissa think about death now, do you think?

9  What is important about Clarissa thinking of herself as "Mrs Richard Dalloway"?

10  Who is Miss Kilman? Why does Clarissa hate her, do you think?

11  What makes Clarissa jump and Septimus stop in the street? What does it tell us about the world at that time?

**1** How do Septimus and Rezia react when the grey car stops outside the flower shop? What do we learn from this about these two characters and their relationship?

**2** When the mysterious grey car passes by, strangers in Bond Street look at each other and think of "their King, their country, the dead". Why do you think they do this, and how do you think they are feeling?

**3** What do people see in the sky behind the aeroplane? What are "Glaxo" and "Kreemo", do you think?

**4** Who is Dr Holmes, and what does he say about Septimus?

**5** When Septimus thinks, "they are making signs to me" what is he looking at? Who do you think "they" are?

**6** Why does Rezia feel so alone?

**1** Why is Clarissa upset by the telephone message she reads when she gets home?

**2** Why does Clarissa sleep in an attic room? What do you think this tells us about Richard and about their marriage?

**3** What sort of person is Sally Seton? What things does Clarissa remember her doing that were shocking? How did Clarissa feel about her at the time?

**4** As she sits sewing, Clarissa says to herself "That is all" and "Fear no more". Look back at these words on page 17. What did she mean then, and what is she thinking about now?

**5** Peter asks Clarissa why she isn't going to invite him to her party, but she doesn't answer. Why do you think that she isn't going to invite him? And why doesn't she answer his question?

**6** "But he never liked anyone who wanted – " What was Clarissa going to say? Why does she stop and say something else?

**7** Clarissa says "Herbert has Bourton now". Who do you think Herbert is?

**8** How does Clarissa feel when Peter tells her that he is in love with Daisy?

**9** What does Peter mean when he thinks, "I know who I am up against"?

**10** Before Elizabeth comes in, Peter says, "Does Richard – " What do you think he is going to ask Clarissa, and why?

## PAGES 38–45

**1** After Peter leaves Clarissa's house, who does he notice as he walks through London? In each case, what is important about these people?

**2** When Peter wakes up and thinks about Bourton again, he remembers saying, "It's got to be finished one way or the other". What did he mean?

## PAGES 45–48

**1** Who is the kind-looking man on the bench next to the little girl and her nanny?

**2** How does Rezia try to help Septimus? How does she feel about doing this?

**3** Who is Evans?

1 What does Peter Walsh think is happening between Rezia and Septimus?

2 What does Peter think about Richard Dalloway? What effect does he think Richard has on Clarissa?

1 What does Rezia think when she first sees the poor old woman singing in the street? And how does she feel after hearing her?

2 What is different about Septimus's character before the War and during it? What happens to him when Evans is killed?

3 What does Septimus think his crimes are? How has he offended Miss Isabel Pole, do you think?

4 What does Dr Holmes "brush aside" when he visits Septimus?

1 Where does Sir William Bradshaw say that Septimus must go, and why?

2 How has Sir William failed Rezia and Septimus, do you think?

1 Why has Lady Bruton invited Richard Dalloway and Hugh Whitbread to lunch?

1 Why does Richard go home after lunch?

2 Which people does Clarissa talk to Richard about because they are making her anxious? What does she worry about after he has gone?

3 What job did Miss Kilman used to have before the War, and why did she have to leave it?

4 What does Miss Kilman feel about Clarissa?

1 What difficulties does Miss Kilman feel that she has?

2 How does Miss Kilman make Elizabeth feel, and why?

3 Where does Elizabeth prefer to be instead of London? Why?

1 What things upset and frighten Septimus?

2 Why is Rezia so happy when Septimus takes the hat from her and laughs?

3 What do you think Septimus means when he cries, "I'll give it to you!"?

1 What does Peter Walsh think about when he sees the ambulance?

2 Why does Peter think it might be better if Daisy doesn't marry him?

3 What reasons does Peter think of for going to Clarissa's party?

1 How do you think the Dalloways' servants feel about the Prime Minister coming to the party?

2 Is Clarissa right that Peter is "in the corner, criticizing her", do you think? Why is she upset by him, do you think?

3 Who is Ellie Henderson, and why has she come to the party?

4 Why does the sight of Ralph Lyon beating back the curtain make Clarissa feel better, do you think?

5 Who is Lady Rosseter, and why is Clarissa so surprised to see her?

6 When Clarissa thinks of the young man she wonders, "had he plunged holding on to what mattered?" What do you think she means by this?

1 In what ways has Sally's character changed from when she was a young woman?

2 What do Sir William Bradshaw and his wife do when they look at a painting?

3 What does Peter think is the difference between being young and old?

# After-reading questions

1 Look back at your answers to "Before-reading questions 1 to 3". Were you right? What other things did you learn from the story about life in 1923?

2 Peter says that Clarissa "had a horror of death". From what we know of her life, why do you think this might be?

3 Clarissa notices the old lady in the house opposite twice (pages 70 and 96). What does this make Clarissa think about? Compare this with the old man staring at Septimus just before he jumps (page 82).

4 Why is Clarissa's party such an important part of the novel, do you think?

5 What was Sally Seton like as a young woman? At the party, how do Clarissa and Peter think she has changed, and how is she the same? What is her importance in the novel?

6 Sally tells Peter, "Clarissa had cared for him more than she ever cared for Richard." Do you think Sally is right?

7 Look at the last words of the novel: "For there she was." What do you think this means? Where have these words been used before? Do you think this is a good ending? Why/Why not?

8 Would you read another novel by Virginia Woolf? Why/Why not?

# Exercises

**1** Complete these sentences with the correct form of the word in your notebook.

| plunge | telegram | extravagant | manner |
|--------|----------|-------------|--------|
| quarrel | mist | pity | upright |

**1** Clarissa remembers a day when she threw open the French windows at Bourton and ........_plunged_........ into the open air.

**2** Clarissa's neighbour sees her standing very ........... by the side of the road, waiting to cross.

**3** Lady Bexborough opened a church fête with a ........... in her hand.

**4** In St James's Park, there is ........... on the lake.

**5** Hugh greets Clarissa ........... when he sees her in the park.

**6** Clarissa remembers often ........... with Peter at Bourton.

**7** Peter criticizes Hugh Whitbread for having nothing but the ........... of an English gentleman.

**8** When Clarissa thinks about Miss Kilman losing her job in the War, she ........... her.

**2** Who is thinking this? Write the correct name in your notebook. (You can use the names more than once.)

| Peter Walsh | Maisie Johnson | Septimus Warren Smith |
| Clarissa | Rezia Warren Smith | Dr Holmes | Lucy |

**1** "Everyone is looking at me because I am standing in their way, but I can't move." <u>*Septimus Warren Smith*</u>

**2** "I miss my family in Italy, and I have nobody to help me here."

**3** "Taking up a sport like cricket will make him feel better."

**4** "I was upset by the strange couple in the park, and I'll always remember it."

**5** "I am sorry to give her a message that I know will upset her."

**6** "When Sally kissed me, I felt as if the world had turned upside down."

**7** "I never got on with her father."

**8** "When he cuts his fingernails with his pocket knife it makes me think he doesn't know what other people are feeling."

**3** Choose the correct adjective to complete these sentences in your notebook.

**1** Peter thinks that the way Clarissa introduced Elizabeth to Peter was **sincere** / **insincere**.

**2** The final bell of St Margaret's Church is loud and **splendid** / **solemn**, which makes Peter think of death.

**3** When Peter follows the young woman in the cloak he feels like a **shy** / **romantic** adventurer.

**4** Peter remembers a quarrel at Bourton, when he was annoyed with Clarissa's cold and **inferior** / **superior** manner.

**5** Rezia finds it strangely **embarrassing / comforting** when the little girl runs into her.

**6** When Septimus looks at Rezia's hand, he looks **terrified / fascinated**.

**7** Peter thinks that Richard is a **brilliant / straightforward** and sensible man.

**8** Clarissa said that seeing her sister killed by a falling tree might have made her **selfish / bitter**.

**PAGES 53–62**

**4 Correct these sentences in your notebook.**

**1** Rezia does not believe that Sir William Bradshaw will be able to help Septimus.

*Rezia feels sure that Sir William Bradshaw will be able to help Septimus.*

**2** Septimus told only his mother when he left his country town for London.

**3** Mr Brewer, Septimus's boss, was about to ask him to leave when the War started.

**4** Evans, Septimus's friend, was killed at the beginning of the War in 1914.

**5** When Septimus heard Rezia crying, he felt unhappy.

**6** Lady Bradshaw would wait at home while her husband visited his patients in the country.

**7** Sir William wants Septimus to go to a nursing home in the country with Rezia.

**8** Sir William was used to the friends and family of his patients feeling disappointed with him.

**5** Complete these sentences in your notebook with the correct form of the past perfect. Use the past perfect simple, continuous or passive.

1 Peter ........*had been*........ (**be**) so much in love with Clarissa and ....*had been rejected*.... (**reject**).

2 Clarissa ........... (**not invite**) Ellie Henderson to her party on purpose, but now Mrs Marsham ........... (**send**) a message.

3 Clarissa told Richard that when Peter Walsh ........... (**visit**), she ........... (**mend**) her dress.

4 Richard and Hugh were at Lady Bruton's because they ........... (**write**) a letter to *The Times* for her.

5 Miss Kilman ........... (**rob**) of happiness.

6 The only happy days of Miss Kilman's life ........... (**spend**) in Germany.

7 Two years and three months ago, Miss Kilman ........... (**go**) into a church and she ........... (**listen**) to the word of God.

8 Clarissa watched the old lady opposite climbing upstairs, as she ........... (**see**) her many times before.

**6** **Match the verbs with their definitions in your notebook.**

*Example:* 1 – *f*

| | | | |
|---|---|---|---|
| **1** | pause | **a** | to make food or drink go from your mouth into your stomach |
| **2** | wrap | **b** | to pull something along the ground in a rough way |
| **3** | ruin | **c** | to bring different things together |
| **4** | swallow | **d** | to pull something out over a large distance |
| **5** | tremble | **e** | to become less strong or clear |
| **6** | drag | **f** | to stop doing something for a short time |
| **7** | stretch | **g** | to put paper, material, etc. around something to cover it |
| **8** | fade | **h** | to destroy something |
| **9** | gather | **i** | to shake slightly |

**7** **Write questions for these answers in your notebook.**

**1** *Who did Rezia and Septimus once find laughing at his papers?*

They found the girl who cleaned the room.

**2** She thinks it's much too small.

**3** Because Septimus had become himself then.

**4** She is Mrs Filmer's grandchild.

**5** She ran downstairs and stood in his way.

**6** Because it would be another of their painful meetings.

**7** She must have written it as soon as Peter left her.

**8** He would write books.

113

**8** Are these sentences *true* or *false*? Write the correct answers in your notebook.

**1** Mrs Barnet has known Clarissa since she moved to Westminster. ..........*false*..........

**2** When the Prime Minister arrives, the guests at the party pretend to ignore him.

**3** Clarissa remembers that Peter and Aunt Helena did not use to get on.

**4** Lady Bruton thinks that Peter Walsh has not made a success of his life.

**5** Clarissa would rather stay and speak to Peter and Sally than go and speak to Lady Bradshaw.

**6** Sometimes Clarissa feels afraid of living life to the end.

**7** Clarissa thinks that Sally is a snob.

**8** Peter thinks he has got over being in love with Clarissa.

**9** Write the correct parts of speech for these words in your notebook.

| | | |
|---|---|---|
| **1** hate (v.) | noun | ..........*hatred*.......... |
| **2** music (n.) | adjective | |
| **3** fail (v.) | noun | |
| **4** comfort (v.) | adjective | |
| **5** suffer (v.) | noun | |
| **6** please (v.) | noun | |
| **7** root (n.) | adjective | |
| **8** quarrel (v.) | noun | |
| **9** young (adj.) | noun | |
| **10** theatre (n.) | adjective | |

**10** Make nouns from these words using these endings:
*-ment, -ence, -ance, -ness.* Draw a table in your notebook.

absent (adj.)    announce (v.)    appear (v.)    careless (adj.)
confident (adj.)    empty (adj.)    important (adj.)
independent (adj.)    ordinary (adj.)    punish (v.)    shy (adj.)
silent (adj.)    tough (adj.)    unhappy (adj.)    wooden (adj.)

|                | *-ment*        | *-ence*   | *-ance* | *-ness* |
|----------------|----------------|-----------|---------|---------|
| absent (adj.)  |                | *absence* |         |         |
| announce (v.)  | *announcement* |           |         |         |
|                |                |           |         |         |

**11** Choose the correct words to complete these sentences
in your notebook.

**1** Oh, if she **could** / **might** have had her life over again, she
thought, stepping on to the pavement; if she **could** / **might**
have even looked different!

**2** "But it's so extraordinary that you **could** / **should** have
come this morning!"

**3** Miss Kilman thought that Mrs Dalloway **might** / **should**
have been in a factory, or in a shop, instead of lying on a sofa.

**4** Who **could** / **should** have imagined it? It was a sudden
decision.

**5** It **might** / **should** have been better if Richard had married
someone who **could** / **should** have helped him more in his
work.

**6** Lady Bruton thought that Peter Walsh was a failure who
**might** / **should** have made a name for himself.

# Project work

1 Think about the sights and sounds that Clarissa or Peter see and hear when they walk through London. (Read pages 11 to 19 and pages 38 to 41 again for ideas.) Then either use your ideas to write a poem about London as shown in the book, or write a detailed description of a place you know well.

2 Look online, and write a newspaper article about women's lives in England in 1923. Include information about:
   • education
   • employment
   • voting

3 Miss Kilman "cared greatly about the state of the Russians and the Austrians". Look online, and make a presentation about what was happening in Russia or Austria in the early 1920s.

4 Watch the film *Mrs Dalloway* (1997) or *The Hours* (2002), and compare the film to the book. What changes have been made, and why?

# Essay questions

- When Virginia Woolf was writing the novel she called it *The Hours*. In what ways is the novel a study of time? (500 words)

- "But it would not have been a success, their marriage." (page 85) Do you think that Clarissa's marriage to Peter would have been a failure? Is her marriage to Richard a success? (500 words)

- Find words and images in the novel that make a connection between Clarissa and Septimus. Why are these images important? How does Virginia Woolf use them to compare these two characters? (500 words)

- Choose three of these characters: Hugh Whitbread, Richard, Elizabeth, Rezia, Lady Bruton, Dr Holmes, Sir William, Lady Bradshaw. Explore how they are shown from different points of view, and explain their importance in the novel. (500 words)

- What do we learn about class (people's position in society and how much money they had) in Britain at this time? (500 words)

- People have said that in Virginia Woolf's novels almost nothing happens. Think about *Mrs Dalloway*. Do you agree or disagree? Give evidence from the book. (500 words)

- Explore how Virginia Woolf moves between the outer and inner world of her characters, and between different characters. What is the effect of this style of writing? Explain why you like or do not like it. (500 words)

An answer key for all questions and exercises can be found at **www.penguinreaders.co.uk**

# Glossary

**aside** (adv.)
1) If you *put* someone *aside*,
they are standing in front of
you but then you move to one
side of them and go quickly
past them.
2) If you *put* or *brush*
something bad or difficult
*aside,* you decide not to think
about it or let it affect you.
3) If a thing or person moves
*aside,* they move away from
something or to one side of it.

**attic** (n.)
a room at the top of a house,
just under the roof

**aware** (adj.)
If you are *aware* of something,
you know that it is there or
happening.

**bark** (v.)
If a dog *barks,* it makes a loud
noise because it is angry or
excited.

**blind** (n.)
a cover that you pull down
over a window

**candlestick** (n.)
a metal or wooden object that
holds a candle

**charming** (adj.)
A *charming* person says and
does nice and interesting
things. A *charming* place is
pleasant and attractive.

**cloak** (n.)
a long, wide coat without
sleeves (= parts that cover
your arms). You wear it
around your shoulders.

**comforting** (adj.);
**comfort** (v. and n.)
If something is *comforting*, or
something or someone *comforts*
you, they make you feel better
when you are sad or worried.
*Comfort* is a feeling of being
less sad or worried about
something. *Comforts* are things
that make your life easier and
more comfortable, like food
or things in your home.

**commit** (v.)
Someone *commits* a crime
when they do something that
is against the law.

**cricket** (n.)
a game played by two teams of 11 players. They win points by hitting a ball with a bat and running between two wickets (= standing sticks).

**criticize** (v.)
to say what you think is wrong or bad about someone or something

**dignity** (n.)
behaving in a calm and serious way which makes other people admire you

**drawing room** (n.)
a room in a large house with a sofa, armchairs, etc. and where guests often sit and talk

**emotion** (n.)
a strong feeling like love, sadness or anger

**extravagant** (adj.);
**extravagantly** (adv.)
1) spending or costing too much money
2) more than usual or necessary.
*Extravagantly* is the adverb of *extravagant*.

**failure** (n.)
when someone or something does not succeed

**fascinate** (v.);
**fascinating** (adj.)
If something *fascinates* you or is *fascinating*, you find it extremely interesting.

**fault** (n.)
1) Something bad has happened because of something that you did. It is your *fault*.
2) something that is not good about a person

**fête** (n.)
a special party outside where you can play games and buy things. Churches and villages sometimes have *fêtes* to get money.

**flu pandemic** (n.)
*Influenza,* or *flu,* is an illness. A *pandemic* is when an illness affects many people across a whole country or the whole world. Millions of people died in the *flu pandemic* between 1918 and 1920.

**foolish** (adj.)
stupid or silly

**fountain** (n.)
A *fountain* pushes water up
into the air and looks pretty.
It is usually in a park or
garden.

**French windows** (n.)
two glass doors that usually
open into a garden

**gather** (v.)
1) If people *gather*, they come
together in one place and
make a group.
2) If you *gather* several things,
you bring them together
from different places.
3) If you *gather* cloth, you sew
it and pull parts of it together
into folds.
4) If you *gather* a person to
you, you pull them towards
you and put your arms
around them.
5) If clouds or waves *gather*,
more of them appear and
they become closer together.

**gaze** (v.)
to look at something for a
long time. *Star-gazing* is the
activity of looking up at stars
and planets in the sky and
studying them.

**get on (with)** (phr. v.)
If two or more people *get on*,
they like each other and are
friendly with each other.

**gift** (n.)
a thing that a person can do
very well

**good heavens** (excl.)
You say *good heavens* when you
are surprised or annoyed.

**hatred** (n.)
a very strong feeling that
you do not like someone or
something

**human nature** (n.)
the ways of feeling, thinking
and behaving that most
people have and are
considered to be normal

**inferior** (adj.)
not as good as another person
or thing

**influenza** (n.)
*Influenza,* or *flu,* is a common (= experienced by a lot of people) illness that makes you feel hot or cold and very weak and tired.

**inner** (adj.)
Your *inner* thoughts, feelings, etc., are private and you don't usually show them to other people.

**insincere** (adj.)
If a person is *insincere,* they say things that they don't really think or believe.

**lace** (n.)
pretty cloth with patterns of small holes in it

**manners** (n.)
Your *manners* are the way that you behave when you are with other people. If you have good *manners*, you behave in a polite way, for example by speaking nicely to someone or opening a door for them.

**Member of Parliament** (n.)
someone who people have elected to work in their country's government

**middle-class** (adj.)
*Middle-class* people are well-educated and own businesses or have good jobs, like doctors, lawyers, etc. They aren't as rich as people from the *upper class,* but they have more money than other people in society.

**mist** (n.)
a lot of very small drops of water in the air. *Mist* looks grey and can make it difficult to see.

**nanny** (n.)
a person, usually a woman, whose job is to look after another person's children

**nursing home** (n.)
a place where people live when they are too old or ill to look after themselves

**one** (pron.)
a formal word used when you are talking about any person in general. It is usually used by *upper-class* people.

**overcome** (v.)
1) If you are *overcome* by an *emotion*, you suddenly feel too much of it.
2) If you *overcome* a problem or difficult thing, you succeed in dealing with it.

**petticoat** (n.)
a thin piece of material that a woman wears under a dress or skirt

**pity** (v. and n.)
to feel sorry for someone because they are in a bad or difficult situation. *Pity* is the noun of *pity.*

**plunge** (v. and n.)
to quickly push or fall down into something. *Plunge* is the noun of *plunge.*

**power** (n.)
to control what happens or what people do

**quarrel** (v. and n.)
If two people *quarrel,* they speak to each other in an angry way because they do not agree. *Quarrel* is the noun of *quarrel.*

**relief** (n.)
the happy feeling that you get because something bad has stopped or has not happened

**root** (n.); **rooted** (adj.)
A *root* is the part of a plant or tree that grows under the ground. It joins it to the ground and keeps it firm. The story describes a person as *rooted* in a place because they don't move from there, like they have *roots* in the ground.

**sake** (n.)
You do something in order to help someone or make them happy. You do it for their *sake.*

**scene** (n.)
a time when people *quarrel,* argue or show strong *emotions*

**self** (n.)
Your *self* is the person you are and what you think and feel. This makes you different from other people. If someone is not their usual *self*, they are ill or unhappy.

**sentimental** (adj.)
showing *emotions* in a way that seems a little silly or unnecessary

**sincere** (adj.);
If a person is *sincere*, they say things that they really think or believe.

**snob** (n.)
a person who thinks they are better than other people because they are in a higher social position

**solemn** (adj.)
serious and sad

**spark** (n.)
1) a small action or idea that causes other things to happen
2) a very small bright light that flies out of something that is burning
3) a small amount of a quality or feeling
4) a person's quality of being lively, intelligent, etc.

**splendid** (adj.)
very beautiful or special

**stand for** (past tense ***stood for***) (phr. v.)
to be an example of something

**state** (n.)
the condition of something or someone at a particular time

**strike** (past tense ***struck***) (v.)
If a clock or bell *strikes*, it rings. When a clock *strikes* three, eleven, etc., it rings three, eleven, etc. times to show that it is 3 o'clock, 11 o'clock, etc.

**superior** (adj.)
1) better than another person or thing
2) thinking that you are better or more important than other people

**surface** (n.)
the top or outside part of something. If a person's *emotions* are on the *surface,* the way they behave or look shows their *inner* feelings.

**telegram** (n.)
in the past, a short, important message that was sent using electricity and printed on paper. In the First World War, people were sent *telegrams* when a soldier from their family had died.

**thud** (v.)
to fall or hit something with a heavy sound. A *thudding* sound is a low, heavy sound that happens again and again.

**toffee** (n.)
a hard brown sweet made by boiling sugar and butter

**tragedy** (n.)
a very sad event or situation which makes people suffer or die

**tremble** (v.)
to shake because you are frightened, nervous or excited

**unaware** (adj.)
If you are *unaware* of something, you do not know that it is there or happening.

**upper-class** (adj. and n.);
If a person is *upper-class* or from the *upper class,* they are part of a group of people who are considered to have the highest position in society and have more money or *power* than other people.

**upright** (adj. and adv.)
1) standing or sitting with a straight back
2) behaving in an honest and responsible way

**upside down** (adv.)
in or into a position where
the part of something that
is usually at the bottom is at
the top. If a person's world is
turned *upside down,* their life
changes completely, often in a
way that is difficult for them.

**youth** (n.)
the time in a person's life
when they are young, or the
quality of being young

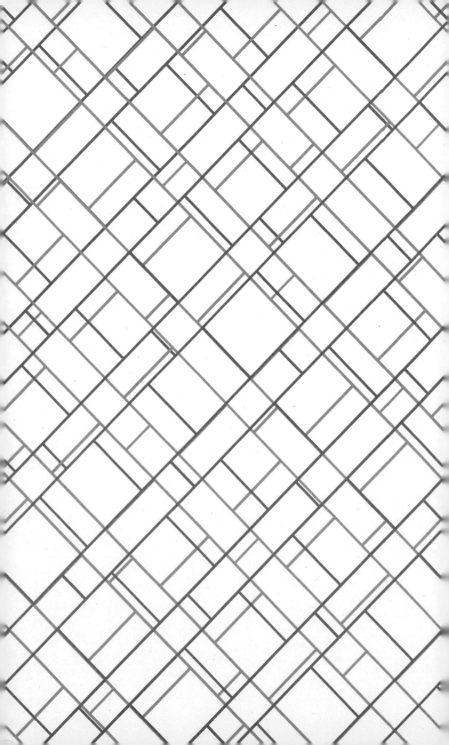

**Penguin** 🐧 **Readers**

Visit **www.penguinreaders.co.uk**
for FREE Penguin Readers resources
and digital and audio versions of this book.